The Figurehead

RDM

The Figurehead

A Story of Conflict and Loyalty at Sea in World War II

Roderick Macdonald

Illustrated by the Author

Roderick Macdonald
Braes Skye 1993

The Pentland Press Limited
Edinburgh · Cambridge · Durham

First published in 1993 by
The Pentland Press Ltd.
1 Hutton Close
South Church
Bishop Auckland
Durham

ISBN 1 85821 056 9

Jacket Illustration by the Author

Typeset by Elite Typesetting Techniques, Southampton.
Printed and bound by Antony Rowe Ltd., Chippenham.

To Jack, the British Sailor

The strength of twice three thousand horse
That serve the one command;
The hand that heaves the headlong force,
The hate that backs the hand.
The doom-bolt in the darkness freed,
The mine that splits the main;
The white-hot wake, the 'wildering speed –
The choosers of the slain.

The Destroyers, Kipling

Battle of the Atlantic
Speech by the author is included with the intention of opening a wider, yet relevant, window on the story of *The Figurehead*.

Published in the year of the Fiftieth Anniversary of the Battle of the Atlantic

Author's profits to King George's Fund for Sailors

Contents

	Acknowledgements	xiii
	Foreword by Admiral of the Fleet, Lord Lewin of Greenwich, K.G., G.C.B., M.V.O., D.S.C.	xvii
	Introduction	xix
Chapters		Page
1	Prelude to Fortune	1
2	Chatty Chats	7
3	Maiden Voyage	17
4	The Quest	30
5	Who Did That?	33
6	Russian Roulette	48
7	You Can't Win	55
8	The Guest Night	60
9	Canteen Boat	73
10	Beating Retreat	84
11	Vigorous Up	89
12	Vigorous Down	104
13	Honk	113
14	Albert	122
15	Edge of the Volcano	129
16	Figgy Duff	135
17	The Figurehead	144
18	Aye Aye	148
19	Soldier Sailor	151
20	The Nancy Brig	153

21	The Grudge Fight	162
22	Round the Bend	168
23	Sippers	171
24	Distance Lends Enchantment	175
25	*Fortune*'s People	179
	Battle of the Atlantic	185
	Notes	192

Maps

A	H.M.S. *Fortune* October 1941 to March 1943, excluding period shown in Map B
B	February 1942 to October 1942

Acknowledgements

The impressions recorded are, to the best of my belief, those that I formed at the time. Subsequent re-appraisal, or information from another source, is indicated in the text or notes. The names of individuals are mainly as I remember them – in some cases only nickname or job title. If I have got any wrong I beg the owner's forgiveness.

It would be impossible to relate in context what amounts to an erratic voyage lasting sixteen months, made long ago and largely out of sight of land, without reference to dates and a track. Private diaries were forbidden in the Navy in World War II for security reasons, as was photography. In 1940 when in uniform, I was arrested in Liverpool for making a drawing of my own ship in drydock. *Fortune*'s records and deck logs, together with those of the rest of her class, apparently went up in smoke in an Admiralty bonfire – perhaps to celebrate the 'end of history'. Fortunately, my father preserved my two untidy astronomical navigation work books for 1941–1943. These provided the data on which to hang the text and put a track on the maps.

The small hard-pressed Naval Historical Branch went out of its way to look for ship movement from another source. These have filled gaps, for which I am most grateful.

In putting something on to paper in 1971 for the Commander-in Chief, Admiral Sir William O'Brien, which might be helpful to officers going in command, I leaned gratefully on a concise booklet written during World War II for the benefit of Reserve Commanding Officers by Lieutenant Commander Hugh Hodgkinson, an experienced destroyer officer, and later Headmaster of Milton Abbey School. Although the events described in *The Figurehead* influenced many pages of *Your Ship*, my own mistakes elsewhere contributed also.

I am indebted to Miss Alexandra Wyke, Ph.D. and Surgeon Commander Rick Jolley, O.B.E., R.N., for ploughing through early drafts of *The Figurehead*, to Mr. and Mrs. Kenneth MacLeod for constructive criticism throughout; to Commander and Mrs. "Bill" Peppe and Sublieutenant Alastair Peppe, R.N., who jointly read the final draft; to my son Alan for his advice, particularly on presentation, and to Miss Ruth Taylor for drawing the maps. I am indebted to my wife, Pamela, for her determined disqualification of incomprehensible maritime jargon.

I also wish to thank all those who have provided essential information, confirmed facts, offered technical advice or given their approval for a reference in the text particularly:

Mr. John A. Agius. National War Museum Malta, G.C.
Captain C.K.S. Aylwin, R.N.
Captain (N.) E. E. Davie, C.D. Canadian High Commission London
Mrs. Brian Gallie
Commander Derek House, M.B.E., D.S.C., F.S.A.
Rear Admiral Richard Hill
Admiral Sir Michael Livesay, K.C.B.
Captain Jock Cunningham, D.S.C., R.N.
Sir Michael Joughin, C.B.E.
Mr. P. Carroll Macnamara
Mr. David Ashby. Naval Historical Branch, Ministry of Defence
Mr. David Taylor. National Maritime Museum
Mr. Paul Kemp. Imperial War Museum
Mr. G. Fordham. Chatham Historic Dockyard Trust
Mr. Andrew Trotman. Royal Naval Museum, Portsmouth
Messrs Curtis Brown and John Farquharson
Mr. David Ellison
Captain Darby George, R.N.
Captain Kenneth Douglas-Morris, R.N.
Admiral Sir Jock Slater, G.C.B., L.V.O.
Commander K. Ridland, R.N.
Messrs Gieves and Hawkes

I have used the following as authorities or for reference, but any mistakes in the text or illustrations are entirely mine:
Engage the Enemy More Closely. The Royal Navy in The Second World War, Correlli Barnett
Memoirs. Ten Years and Twenty Days. Doenitz
Merchantmen Rearmed. David Bone

Operation Drumbeat. Michael Gannon
Maritime Forces Supporting Malta 1940–1943. CKS Aylwin
Navi E Marinai Italiani. Elio Ando Eminio Bagnasco
The Second World War. Churchill
The Red Duster. John Slader
The Man Around the Engines. Vice Admiral Sir Louis Le Bailly

Foreword

Roddy Macdonald and I have been close friends since the very start of our Naval lives; even so I was touched that he should ask me to contribute a Foreword to this account of a somewhat troublesome period of his career. We joined the Training Cruiser *Frobisher* in the same Special Entry batch; looking back, two things first drew us together, the juxtaposition of L and M in the alphabet and a shared passion for rugby football. It was the first, I guess, that appointed us both to the brand new cruiser *Belfast* in August 1939. From her we went on together to *Valiant* and thence in the summer of 1941 to abbreviated Sub-Lieutenants Courses at Portsmouth. The varied experiences of those two and a half years and many common interests had cemented our friendship.

Then we went our separate ways: Roddy to *Fortune* to serve with a Commanding Officer who was everything that a Captain should not be, where he endured all the events that are described in this book; I, by way of a short period in a Western Approaches escort and a dose of diptheria, to a Tribal class destroyer in the Home Fleet commanded by Dicky Onslow, a legend among World War Two destroyer Captains.

For two years we corresponded little if at all. We were serving in widely separated theatres and busy, mail was slow and letter writing reserved for girl friends and family – in that order. By remarkable coincidence, in the early summer of 1943 my ship followed *Fortune* into the London Graving Dock for a refit. We were soon back in touch and have remained so ever since.

Roddy didn't specialise, he stayed a salt horse, a professional seaman. He went on to command a number of ships, first as a Lieutenant Commander, rare for those post-war days, and in command he put right all the things that were wrong in *Fortune*. So conspicuous was his success that he was selected for the post of Commander Sea Training, a key appointment in the relatively new ship work up organisation at Portland, where newly commissioned ships were taught how a ship should be run. In the fullness of time, after five ship commands and the Joint Service command of all the Maritime Forces off Borneo during the period of confrontation with Indonesia, now a senior Captain, he was chosen for the post of Captain of the Fleet at Fleet Headquarters Northwood, one of those inspired appointments that give faith in the system.

It was the responsibility of the Captain of the Fleet to be the Commanding Officer's friend at court, someone of great experience to whom the ship Captain could turn for advice and help; while to the Commander-in-Chief he was the Staff Officer with his finger on the pulse of the Fleet, giving early warning of the little niggles that could affect morale, able to advise on the strengths and weaknesses of the ships and squadrons.

As Captain of the Fleet Roddy was the roundest of pegs in a round hole, but perhaps his greatest contribution while in this appointment was to write a book, another book called *Your Ship*. Designed to be the new Commanding Officer's guide on how to be a good Captain. it was based on an accumulation of experience and contained the sea-wisdom that properly followed will point the new Captain to a happy and successful commission. *Your Ship* has performed this function now for nearly twenty years, the message has not changed, and it has, I am sure, been kept handy beside many a Captain's bunk.

Reading *The Figurehead* some will wonder that such things could ever happen, but contained here is a moral that every young Naval Officer should heed: there is always something to be learnt from example, be the example good or bad.

If only "Honk" could have read *Your Ship*. . . .

Admiral of the Fleet Lord Lewin, K.G., G.C.B., M.V.O., D.S.C.
Suffolk. January 1993

Introduction

One night recently I rushed to Action Stations from the charthouse – and then woke up in bed in Skye. The noise created by a seventeenth century grandfather clock preparing to strike midnight resembles that made by a Second World War destroyer's revolution telegraph. The chains connecting this contraption to the engineroom passed through the charthouse, where I had slept at sea fifty years ago. Their peremptory rattle and "ding, ding, ding" was a signal that the Officer of the Watch required high speed in a hurry.

I started to put this story down the next day. It is true but there are several unhappy and disturbing incidents which contrast with what passes for normality at sea. The Royal Navy cannot always be perfect. For a war story it is short on shot and shell, and no medals for gallantry are won or deserved. Britain was in retreat and many elsewhere in the world thought near defeat. It was the very nadir of the war. Our heroine *Fortune* had already earned three Battle Honours – Norway, Atlantic and Malta Convoys. Sailors believe that some ships are lucky and others are not. A "lucky ship", she carried us safely over many hostile seas for a year and a half, to live and fight another day. The only hero was Jack, who put up with much, or anyway did so for most of the time.

Braes, Isle of Skye. 1993

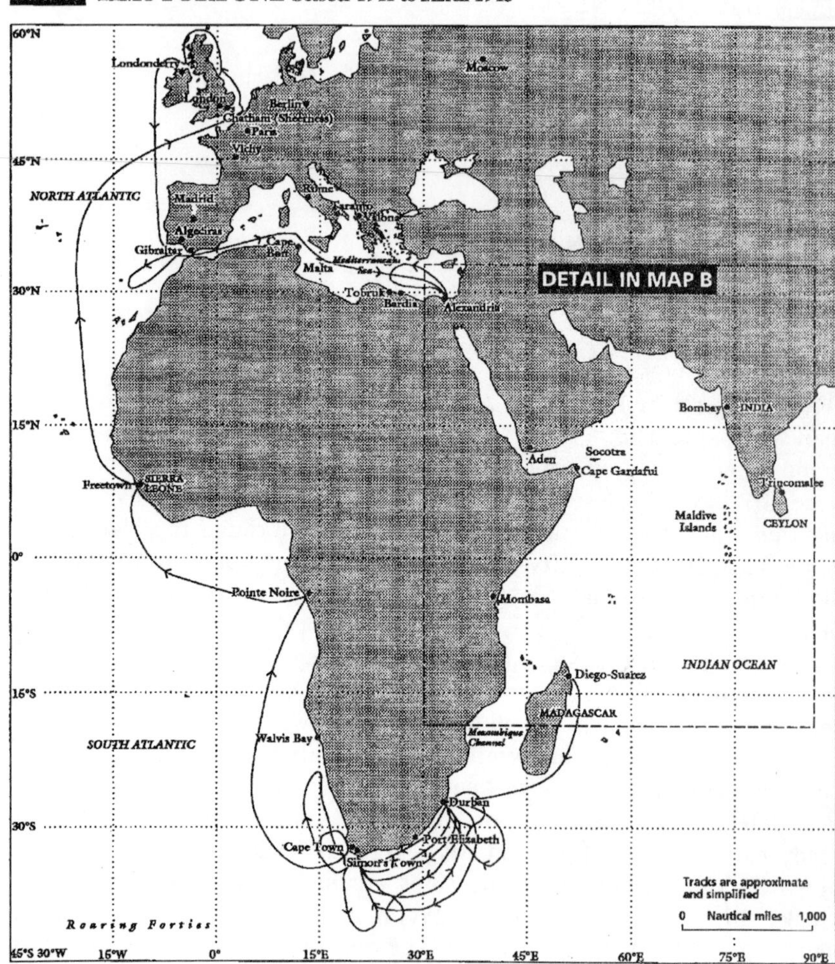

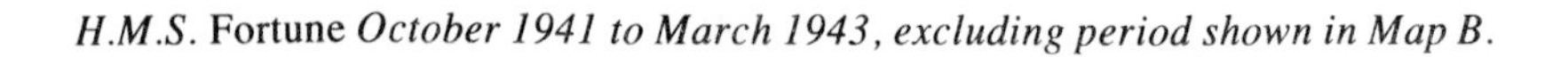
H.M.S. Fortune *October 1941 to March 1943, excluding period shown in Map B.*

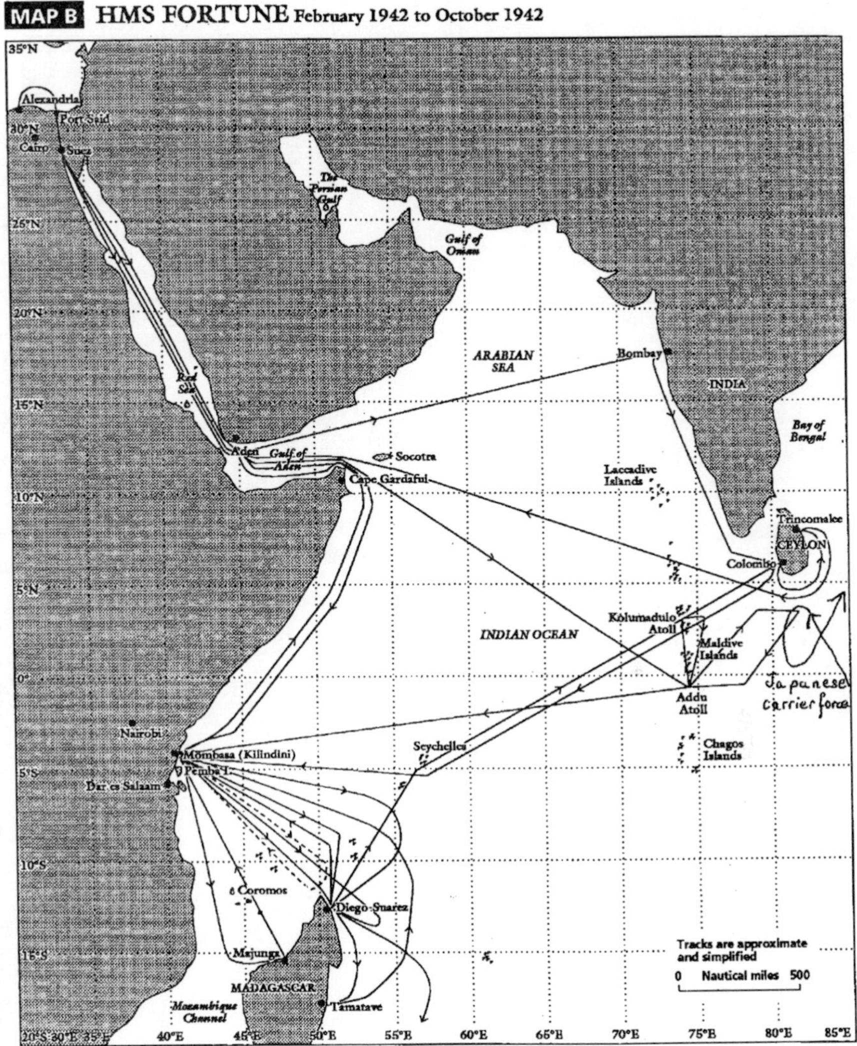

February 1942 to October 1942.

Chapter 1

Prelude to *Fortune*

He put in his thumb, pulled out a plum
And said what a good boy am I!

Even in 1941, in the middle of a World war – a war, which as far as the Navy was concerned, had never been phoney – the Admiralty maintained a sense of style. The most insignificant officer was encouraged to call

at the office of the Naval Secretary in Queen Anne's Mansions by St. James's Park to discuss his next appointment and how it might affect a vestigial career.

Self-consciously wearing the new straight gold lace single stripes of an acting sublieutenant, I presented myself by appointment and waited anxiously for my turn. Meanwhile I passed the time trying to distinguish senior officers from office messengers. Both categories shared maturity and wore anonymous black alpaca jackets. To me, a nobody, the messengers seemed supercilious, but the Appointer,[1] whose business it was to know everybody in the business however humble, turned out to be avuncular and even optimistic about granting my wish to be sent to a destroyer, "any old destroyer, sir, anywhere." Later I wondered if there had not been just a suspicion of sardonic amusement within the half promise that I was granted. But I had no premonition of anything untoward.

The following paragraphs give some idea of my brief naval experience before joining this longed-for destroyer. That I had never been on board a destroyer was not important.

"Recruited" when I was four years old by a visit of His Majesty's cruiser *Hawkins* to Sourabaya in Java, I had passed the Special Entry exam into the Royal Navy from Fettes when I was seventeen, joining the training cruiser *Frobisher* in January 1939. One training cruise to Iceland and Brittany in *Vindictive* followed when we met our contemporaries from Dartmouth,[2] before recall from summer leave as war with Germany was virtually certain.

As a cadet and midshipman my war so far (amounting to eighteen months) had been spent in a cruiser, a steam drifter and a battleship. First in the 6-inch gun cruiser, *Belfast*,[3] on Northern patrol until her back was broken off May Island in 1939 by the first successful U-boat-laid German magnetic mine. During this period I enjoyed an interlude seconded to

Lunar Bow, an armed steam drifter, patrolling the entrance to Scapa Flow through which Prien's U-boat entered to sink the *Royal Oak*. We were sailed for Loch Ewe the day before this tragedy, but not before informing the Admiral by signal about the two separate gaps in the blockship defences of Kirk Sound through which a submarine could enter on the surface[4] at high water spring tides.

On leaving *Belfast* my confidential report recorded "this officer plays the bagpipes". Their Lordships shortly drew the Captain's attention to the regulations, which clearly state that "adverse reports should be underlined in red ink". Since my early *Hawkins* experience, an enjoyment of *The Wonder Book Of The Navy*, followed by reading authors such as Taffrail, Bartimeus and Keble Chatterton, had filled me with admiration for the service, which the muddles in Scapa Flow had done little to reinforce.

Then with my fellow cadet friend, Midshipman Terry Lewin,[5] I was sent immediately to join the modernised battleship *Valiant* (eight 15-inch and twenty 4.5-inch guns and the second ever seaborne air warning radar). She was blessed with two outstanding officers, Captain Henry Bernard Rawlings[6] and Commander Peter Reid.[7] We only just caught our ship leaving Devonport as she sailed unescorted through an Atlantic gale with dockyard workers still on board, sea water flooding the unfinished 4.5-gun casemates, to work up off Bermuda. After this she escorted a convoy of big troopships, including *Aquitania*, from freezing Halifax to the Clyde, where degaussing (protection from magnetic mines) was fitted. Then followed the chaotic Norwegian campaign, which we suspected correctly to be a political and joint service cockup, and in which *Valiant* provided defence for large military convoys and the Home Fleet. She was bombed constantly in and off the fiords, while with the Fleet she searched everywhere, high and low, for the German navy. Of them, we saw only the crew of a U-boat sunk by a destroyer on the screen. The C.O. was a rampant Nazi. He thought it very unfair that he had been caught on the surface as we came round a corner in a narrow fiord. His crew were not too unhappy about becoming prisoners of war.

The luckless C.in.C Home Fleet, Admiral Sir Charles Forbes, regularly starved (although we did not know this at the time) of essential Intelli-

gence by the Admiralty, got known unfairly as Wrong Way Charlie,[8] – even as Fifth Column Forbes by my Royal Marine "servant". Afterwards *Valiant* joined Force H at Gibraltar, Admiral Sir James Somerville, taking part in the sad, but essential, destruction of the French Fleet at Mers el Kebir (Oran).[9] This busy period, followed by the relief of Malta escorting a large convoy, and then on through to Alexandria to join the Mediterranean Fleet, is covered in my Midshipman's journal.[10]

Activity under the command of Admiral Sir Andrew Cunningham included bombardments of Bardia in support of the army in the Western Desert and of Valona, in the Adriatic, together with frequent, but abortive, sweeps through the Mediterranean in attempts to catch the shy Italian navy at sea. We supported *Illustrious* during her brilliantly successful Swordfish torpedo attack on the Italian fleet in Taranto, on which the Imperial Japanese Navy modelled its unexpected aerial descent on Pearl Harbour.

Throughout *Valiant* remained unscathed under continuous German and Italian bombing. The gunroom played deck hockey on the quarterdeck in the afternoon between attacks, called to action by bugle. She was a successful and happy ship with a splendid captain and good officers, with a gunroom run in a civilised manner.[11] I was lucky to have served in her as a midshipman, although allocation to what we were led to believe were

indispensable Action Stations was the unusually flattering reason for denying both Terry Lewin and myself our stipulated and sought after detachment to destroyers. During high level attacks by German bombers in a clear blue sky off Norway, we were both posted at the back of the bridge with binoculars to alert the captain. "Bomb doors open, sir." Then "Bombs Away!" He then put the wheel hard over one way or the other. It always worked, as the explosions and columns of water erupted where we would otherwise have been. Teutonic aviators are notably precise. Rawlings remains my ideal Warship Captain.

Our batch of midshipmen took the Fleet Board Seamanship exam. for the rank of Lieutenant on board the flagship *Queen Elizabeth* in Alexandria harbour. Understandably confident in practical seamanship – in my view the real thing – I got my "come-uppance" when the courteous President, Captain Cooke (who soon after, poor man, went down with his ship, *Barham*, torpedoed by a U-boat) told me that, owing to my lack of knowledge of destroyers and supply and secretariat subjects, the latter requiring memorisation and detail which I had considered a waste of time – can look it up in a book – he could only award me a Second Class certificate. I knew that it was my own fault for not paying attention to the syllabus, together with too much enthusiasm for what interested me at the expense of what did not – much the same as at Fettes, where rugger, painting, Ruskin and Churchill's *Life of Marlborough* had attracted my attention to the exclusion of algebra and Latin.[12]

Chapter 2

Chatty Chats

I saw a ship a' sailing,
A' sailing on the sea,
And Oh but it was laden
With pretty things for thee . . .

So on Trafalgar Day, 21 October 1941, I stood in Chatham dockyard, known to Jack as Chatty Chats, looking down into a cavernous dry dock. Below, shored up by a small forest of wooden beams, and festooned with compressed air pipes, wires, red lead paint, and serenaded by rivet hammers in a deafening concerto, lay His Majesty's Ship *Fortune*. She was near the end of six months of bomb damage repair required after fighting a convoy to Malta in May that year.

After leaving *Valiant* in Alexandria,[1] my contemporaries and I had enjoyed a luxurious, and at times hilarious, trip back to the U.K. from Alexandria round the Cape via Durban in R.M.S. *Monarch Of Bermuda*.[2] Some abbreviated technical courses in weaponry, signals, navigation and ceremonial square-bashing followed, mainly at Portsmouth – dozing at desks after fire-watching during nightly air raids, and hoping it would not rain owing to there being no roof but a tarpaulin over the damaged classroom.[2]

Below me now was a standard prewar destroyer, of which there were several nearly identical classes with nine ships in each. The classes were formed into flotillas, each with a leader bigger than the others to accommodate staff. She had been launched in 1933,[3] displaced 1,375 tons and was 329 feet over all in length. *Fortune* was designed for high speed with 36,000 shaft horsepower, six times greater than the destroyers in Kipling's powerful lines. She was capable of thirty-six knots, but this would have been achieved in a flat calm on the measured mile. Her designated role was to protect our own battle fleet and attack the opposing battleships with torpedoes. I could see two tall funnels and even taller masts, four 4.7-inch calibre guns in single open mountings, four torpedo tubes (dictating a low freeboard and a narrow beam of thirty-three feet and thus a wet upper deck), two Oerlikon automatic eyeball-aimed anti-aircraft guns with a single primitive 3-inch A.A. gun where another set of torpedoes used to be, and two depth charge throwers down aft. The white ensign hung limply from her main-mast gaff showed that she was in commission.

The design, a World War One throw back, was already historic, particularly in air defence. But she did carry on her foremast an early rotating air warning R.D.F. (radar)[4] and underneath her keel an Asdic (Sonar) dome. These and other modifications had increased her complement from 150 to over 180 without any significant adjustment to living arrangements. Proportionately a third of her volume contained propulsion machinery, a third her armament and magazines, and the remaining third included living space, store rooms, galley and offices. Any limitations could not diminish either my excitement or pride. To me she looked wonderful. Scattered nearby, labelled *Fame*, were the bits and pieces of a sister ship, which had recently embedded herself in Northumberland owing to taking a wrong turning in fog. A rattle of metal behind me disturbed my train of thoughts.

A medium-sized, immaculately uniformed naval officer in his early thirties, wearing the straight gold two-and-a-half stripes of an R.N. Lieutenant Commander, looked down at me from a pyramid of rusty iron plates, corroded chain cable and steel bolts. His glossy black hair was smoothly plastered down. Under the shadow of the peak of his neat uniform cap, dark eyes moved restlessly from one side to the other. His nose was sharp and his arms hung down from his shoulders, reminding me of the wings of a perched raven. He did not seem to be a cheerful person. I realised instinctively that this was the captain. I came to attention and saluted.

He obviously knew who I was but he made no attempt to introduce himself, to say hello, or communicate socially. In staccato he announced, "Sub, you are to take on Navigation, and of course Signals and Torpedo Control. The ship is to be ready for sea in all respects in four weeks."

My heart sank. I did feel reasonably confident in coastal pilotage and in waggling a sextant in tune with a deck watch. But to avoid having my shore leave, a rare commodity, stopped as a punishment by *Valiant*'s Instructor Commander, I had become, like a number of my contemporaries, adept at fudging the arithmetical calculations that are required to turn celestial altitudes into terrestrial position lines, a deceptive backward computation for which no understanding of basic theory is necessary.[5] My excuse was that we had been at the time watchkeeping for four hours "on" and four hours "off", interspersed with action stations at dawn, at dusk, and whenever the enemy turned up. In harbour it had been more fun running the picket boats and launch than falling asleep over columns of logarithms.

I was therefore scarcely overwhelmed with confidence in my ability to find where a ship was at any particular time on the surface of the ocean. On the other hand, during technical courses I had discovered what I felt sure was a flair for anti-submarine warfare, and had even basked in unaccustomed credit from Teacher.[6] Seeing myself as a born U-boat killer, I was disappointed to be denied this opportunity for instantaneous and heroic fulfilment. But as was to be often the case, a job chosen for me by higher authority, unappreciated at the time, turned out later to my advantage.

I was now uneasy. The cold, formal, unsmiling, even grim impression created by the C.O. did not fit in with my idealised image of a "Salt Horse" (non-specialist) destroyer captain. This mental picture was formed partly from legend, but largely from watching these extrovert heroes manoeuvre their exciting commands around the big ships of the fleet at sea, and when they berthed alongside with a flurry of astern power – high speed one minute, then stopped and secured fore and aft without so much as a tremor.

"Oh," he added, "I asked for the Surgeon Lieutenant to be a young one, so that you can have someone about your own age on board."

I was touched by this unexpected example of thoughtfulness and immediately felt guilty about any qualms that I might have felt. Then without another word he turned abruptly, disappearing from view behind the mound of metal with a clank, A small cloud of orange-coloured rust settled where he had just been. Navigation. Horrors! Suddenly the tangled bits and pieces of His Majesty's Ship *Fame* scattered about the dockyard nearby took on a sinister significance.

What he did during the next four weeks I do not know, but I barely saw the captain again before we sailed. Nor, I suspected, did anyone else.

Meanwhile I did my best to get to know the signal (visual), telegraphist (radio), and R.D.F. (radar) ratings in my division as well as their equipment. I also found that it was necessary to drum up warm clothing, essential for Jack's survival when exposed to the weather. These were described officially as Comforts, perhaps because they were not provided by the Government. I discovered a source of woollies, all voluntarily knitted by the ladies of Guildford, who were at first reluctant providers as they considered themselves as knitters for the army. In exchange I bartered two Italian army rifles which I had "liberated" in North Africa. These were soon removed from the W.V.S. shop window display. Their obvious obsolescence apparently did little to enhance our gallant Army's reputation, at the time based on its routing of General Graziani.

I was also hard at it, working late, in the unfinished chart house inserting, from information provided by Q.Z. messages, the minefields (theirs and ours), and swept channels on all charts for a passage up the east coast of England and round Scotland to Londonderry. This was to be our first port of call on the way to Gibraltar to join Force H. There was a potential requirement to enter every minor port *en route* in the event of action damage. (Later on in the war, ships would have our own "friendly" minefields officially printed in purple before the charts were supplied.)

The captain seemed to have a naive confidence, which I certainly did not share, in his youthful navigating officer. He never checked my work, as he should have done, both to comply with the regulations and with commonsense. There was no flotilla[7] staff that I could find in Chatham to consult, and this worried me. I referred to my mentor, Captain J.A.G. Troup's splendid book *On The Bridge*.[8] The Preface was clear enough.

> "There is no doubt as to the responsibility of the Captain of any one of the H.M. ships. It is clearly defined in the King's Regulations and Admiralty Instructions:
>
> 'The Captain is responsible for the safe conduct and steering of the ship which he commands.
>
> 'The Navigating Officer, under the direction of the Captain, is to have charge of the Navigation of the ship.
>
> 'In ordinary circumstances the Navigating Officer is the Pilot of the ship.'
>
> "This latter Regulation applies only to qualified Navigating Officers."

I was not one of these mature lieutenants, who had passed a Long (N) specialist qualifying course. Realising that I would not accumulate many marks for tact were I to draw the captain's attention to this regulation, I confided in the First Lieutenant. Quite apart from what was stipulated in K.R. & A.I., I suggested, I did not deserve, because of my inexperience, such total trust, especially in view of the consequences in the event of a navigational mistake or just as a result of my general ignorance. Would he please help? I added that a more experienced sublieutenant, the navigator, in the destroyer alongside, was equally hard pressed now and showing irritation at my many elementary and time-consuming questions.

It was clear that the First Lieutenant was under unusual pressure. He told me he thought I seemed to be setting about things the right way, but he genuinely could not spare any time to vet my chart work. There was a popular song about a damaged R.A.F. bomber returning home on a wing and a prayer. I noted that *Fortune*'s heraldic crest consisted of a wheel equipped with a wing, but ominously no sign of any prayer.

Lieutenant Michael Morris had only recently transferred to the Royal Navy from the Merchant Navy (Khedivel Mail Line) under the Emergency, but successful, Scheme jokily known as the Hungry Hundred. He was a fully qualified Master Mariner, experienced seafarer and entertaining raconteur of outrageous salty stories, most of which turned out to be true.[9] His father, Morris Bey, had sported a tarbush as Chief Engineer officer of the Egyptian Royal Yacht.

I soon realised that Michael was good with the sailors and firm when he had to be, a likable and stable personality with an open florid face, clear blue eyes under sandy eyebrows and flat feet, which provided stability in a seaway. He possessed an enviable ability to transmit a picturesque stream of seafaring abuse in Arabic and other languages without repeating himself. He had only served in one appointment in the Royal Navy, apart from technical courses, before finding himself second in command of a fleet destroyer. His detailed knowledge of the Grey Funnel Line, he maintained, was as minimal as mine. I doubted that this could be possible.

Detail was not the metier of Lieutenant Philip (Tiny) Archer-Shee, who as Number Two was next in line. Immensely tall, well-built, eloquent, handsome, an Etonian and member of the Carlton Club, he had been a peacetime R.N.V.R., done something in the City and was well off, or seemed to be. He had a fertile brain, an engaging personality and was adept at avoiding serious work. His responsibilities seemed to be confined to confidential books, cryptography and keeping us entertained.

Of the three remaining officers (not counting the doctor), the Engineer was balding, thickset Lt. Commander (E) C.F.I. Batt, Royal Naval Reserve. In his forties and much the oldest, he revelled in informing the world that his civilian occupation was charge of the boilers and machinery of a lunatic asylum and that his name was appropriate.

The correspondence, pay and anti-submarine officer, a peacetime R.N. V.R. in his thirties, was Lieutenant Mathews. A kind, rather gentle bachelor, his career in the soft fruit trade, some of whose commodities his face vaguely resembled, may have been responsible for an endless repertoire of double entendre and nickname of Porny. This had not exactly prepared him for the "oranges and lemons and here comes a chopper to chop off your head" party game of destroyer life in war. Good with paper and thoughtful about his sailors, he seemed at times professionally unsure, and nervous, with an amazing ability in such a small ship to go to ground like a hunted fox.

The acting torpedo gunner, Ernest Pinnock, a warrant officer (one thin gold stripe), straight from the Lower Deck and serving in his first ship as an officer, was exactly as he should have been; utterly reliable, knowledgeable, funny and always helpful. He was nicknamed Fred because Philip Archer-Shee claimed rather grandly this to have been standard nomenclature for all Gunners (T) in his previous up-market, and much boasted about, "Tribal" flotilla. Fred claimed to be small enough to walk under the torpedo tubes without removing his cap; also that when he and his appendix were separated the surgeon threw away the wrong bit. Walt Disney probably used his rubicund, cheerfully wrinkled features and snub nose to model one of the Seven Dwarfs. Fred, who unusually for a gunner, did not drink, was married, as were the First Lieutenant and Engineer Officer. The others were bachelors. The Wardroom looked to be a promising mix.

Until the ship became habitable we lived in the Royal Naval Barracks, which were largely occupied by young doctors learning how to salute and what seemed immensely elderly officers recalled from civil life. Whiskers grew out of their ears, as they do from mine now. I shared a cabin happily with a near contemporary, Derek Kent,[10] Sublieutenant of the submarine *Taku* sitting in a nearby dry dock. Years later he told me that we had been ticked off by the formidable First Officer W.R.N.S. for not saluting her (not actually then a regulation). Apparently I had replied impertinently that I only "took my hat off to ladies".

Accustomed as the Royal Navy is now to an elaborate and intensive programme of sea trials, shake-down and several weeks "work up" of

weapon systems and operational efficiency for a ship after major refit or recommissioning with a new crew, it is interesting to remember that in wartime a refitted warship left Chatham dockyard for Sheerness Naval Base one day; ammunitioned, fuelled and "swung" (adjusted) the magnetic compass on the next two. Then the following morning she was on her own, at sea, a vulnerable newcomer in a hostile world, depth charges primed and warheads fitted to torpedoes. *Valiant* in December 1939 had sailed from Devonport to Bermuda unescorted in much the same condition, a monster of a sitting duck.[11]

It was amazing that most things actually worked. Of course they could have worked much better. Many of the sailors had never been to sea before. A sprinkling of experienced, and to my eyes, impressive senior ratings, Chief Petty Officers, Petty Officers and Artificers, made it possible. Humour abandoned, although there was not much to joke about. Our people had followed on from a dockyard organisation, which confidently refitted a collection of obsolescent, but for this reason familiar, machinery and weapons. Dockyard workers, I was cynically informed by older hands, proceeded at measured pace, taking their times from the dockyard clock within regular working hours regardless of the news, good or bad. They had a point. It was going to be a long war.

The evening before leaving Sheerness Petty Officer Telegraphist Wildsmith, who thought in Morse code and never used two words when one would do, asked my permission to go some distance to say goodbye to his wife and family. He assured me that he had rigged and matched his "roof" aerials and organised watchkeeping on all the required frequencies. The ship was now "under sailing orders", with shore leave restricted to the immediate locality. Wildsmith was an irreplaceable member of the team, so this bending of the rules, which I suspected, rightly, was not anyway within my bailiwick, was for me a crucial decision. I trusted him, and he did not then, or at any time later, let me down. Soon there was to be a close shave involving the wireless world, but not his fault.

Fortune was in no way ready to fight a battle or even defend herself. How lucky it seemed that the opposition did not know. Soon it became too evident that there was no need. A prolific potential for self-inflicted wounds abounded.

Chapter 3

Maiden Voyage

Alone, alone, all, all alone,
Alone on a wide, wide sea.
Ancient Mariner

An unqualified navigator's first voyage is for him a special and unforgettable event. Preparations for sailing kept me up late and got me up early. The 28th November 1941 was typically cold but windless. Several ships of the local flotilla were pencilled delicately on a silver sea. Here and there, a sinister collection of masts and derricks projected out of the water at eccentric angles alongside the fairway, evidence of recent enemy success with mine and bomb. I scuttled about double checking, not always necessarily, the compass, the navigation lights, the recognition signal, the torpedo control – the last in case of an inadvertent rendezvous with *Hipper* – and much minutiae. The fo'c's'le lockerman, Stripey, an able

seaman wearing three Good Conduct Badges, who was old enough to be my father, reported that the stand-by oil navigation lights were placed and correct. He doubled as lamp-trimmer, for which he earned an extra penny a day. This was an arcane task in wartime when even the main navigation lights were not used. On the dot came the signal IJ "Approved to proceed".

We had just slipped from the buoy, and turned to head for sea, when a despatch boat came alongside and threw a bulky, unmarked for precedence, brown envelope on board. This contained a heap of general messages transmitted before the ship's own radio watch was set, and thus the responsibility of the shore staff to provide. From the pencilled figures in my notebook I read out the various courses for the captain to steer down the swept channel to the gate in the Medway anti-submarine boom, which was just visible through mist a few miles ahead.

Suddenly the boom vessel controlling the gate came to life, flashing repeatedly the letter U (You are standing into danger). Horrors! *Fortune* went astern fast. As the person responsible for both navigation and signals, I was convinced that my career, if not the ship, was already up for grabs. The flickety flick of the signal lamp spelled out "Enemy mine field laid just ahead of you. QZ message number so and so refers." I was stunned. Meanwhile, the Yeoman of Signals, Petty Officer Cromwell, had fished from the envelope, in amongst administratively important matters, such as an increase in the victualling price of potatoes, a signal labelled "Priority" and not "Immediate", as it should have been, announcing a new enemy minefield laid by air in the swept channel just ahead.

While, with what confidence remained, I plotted an alternative route through the mudbanks to reach the degaussing (protection against magnetic mines) range in the Thames estuary, I kicked myself for not having asked the captain to stop the ship until the contents of the albeit routinely marked envelope had been digested. It was of course quite wrong to have passed such an urgent warning in so casual a manner. For some time afterwards I treated shore-based services with unnecessary suspicion, but I had learned a lesson. Meanwhile, our C.O. relieved himself by letting off loud volumes of steam in different directions. Whether or not he felt at all guilty, I would never know.

This and certain other signs of a short fuse could, I thought, have been generated by the understandable pressures of a first command. It was certainly different from what I had come to believe was the norm in my perhaps idealised navy and which I had been accustomed to in my last ship.

The degaussing serial, essential to avoid activating magnetic mines, was hurried. I felt sorry for the poor, chilled-to-the-bone, range officer employed on such a repetitive and boring task, while we would be gallivanting off to unimaginable and glamorous adventures. In reality he would soon wend his way thankfully home to an ever loving wife and toasted crumpets. Halfway through the serial, while the ship was turning 180 degrees in the narrow channel, the steering gear failed. Changeover drill to steering by hand and mechanical wheel from aft had been correctly practised before leaving harbour. It worked, but somewhat slowly. We anchored abruptly next to a sinister and slimy mudbank. On this occasion an unhappy First Lieutenant and sardonic Engineer Officer were at the receiving end of the captain's violently expressed displeasure as were any ratings who accidentally came within his line of fire. These incidents and accompanying choreography must have provided Jack with something to talk about, but were unlikely to have contributed to his confidence in the Management. From now on it was obvious that the ship's company did its best to avoid the Captain.

I knew that I was the only officer with some involvement in, and even responsibility for, each of these incidents. The curious part was that I had not attracted flak while others with less or no responsibility had. Perhaps as an acting sublieutenant I was too small a cog to count – just a learner, which indeed was true. The Wardroom loyally pretended that nothing particularly odd had happened.

Fortune wended her way north at twenty knots up the swept channels that I had plotted with great care and some anxiety from The Nore to John-o'-Groats. The sea was smooth. The ship's machinery drummed and hummed rhythmically. On each different leg our

wake lay straight astern like cream spooned into a coffee-coloured sea over which gulls quarrelled noisily for lunch. We overtook and passed that day's north-bound convoy, several miles long in line ahead and consisting mainly of empty colliers, bound for refill at Methyl – flatirons with the sort of hinged funnel that can be lowered to clear a Thames bridge; their escort two veteran V and W class destroyers, one ahead and one astern.

I was more or less constantly on the bridge. This structure was a metal box open to the sky and the weather, its internal sides festooned with a multitude of brass-bound dials, instruments, telephones and bell-mouthed voice pipes labelled with engraved tallies, also in brass. Everything looked as if it had been designed to take the weight of a performing elephant. The dials were impossible to read in the dark, particularly when encrusted with salt and verdigris. Forward there was a badly-lit, hooded

enclosed table, craftily designed to be not quite large enough to take an unfolded Admiralty chart. Newly installed orange lighting (beneficial for night vision) I was to discover shortly would obliterate all symbols, including minefields inserted in red (the colour we had been instructed to use). Underneath, a sort of rabbit hutch contained the Asdic (sonar) control instruments and their operator. From this the next day would emerge a ping sound with which we lived at sea, getting anxious if it stopped. At present in depths too shallow for submarines, it was silent and switched to hydrophone, listening for the sound of German E-boat[1] propellers.

The bridge desk with its scrubbed wooden gratings, designed to allow surplus sea water to drain away, accommodated the gyro and magnetic compass binnacles as well as the dramatis personae. This consisted of the captain, when circumstances required his presence, the officer of the watch, me as navigator, a signalman, two lookouts and a messenger. The last was important because he called your relief and made the cocoa. The signalman was constantly on the run, particularly when *Fortune* was in company with other ships. Apart from communicating with the wireless office down a voicepipe (up which incoming messages were pulled by a string), he conducted visual signalling such as flag hoisting, flashing and semaphore, at the same time coding and decoding everything except what was self-evident. At Action Stations I took over as officer of the watch, as well as remaining the navigator. I was later to discover that such a combination was unworkable, because tactical control, as well as ship command, was in those days exercised totally from the bridge. As Officer of the Watch, I was responsible for the safety of the ship. As Navigator, I was supposed to advise the Captain on her tactical handling and the conduct of operations. Both activities required anticipation of the unexpected.

Looking towards the bows, protection from the elements was about chest high. A combination of speed and weather often allowed a generous mixture of seawater and wind to share the stage and penetrate oilskin collars and sea boot tops. When the wind howled through the rigging and superstructure the resulting noise required a great deal of shouting at a volume which would have done justice to a parade ground. The quartermaster (helmsman), engine room telegraph rating and plotter inhabited the wheelhouse one deck below, from which via the voicepipe a pungent aroma of duty free cigarette smoke emerged, enriched once every twenty-four hours by the scent of Nelson's blood (the rum ration). The helmsman could see out directly ahead through a scuttle (port hole). This ensured concentration when following in line ahead in close order (300 yards) at

high speed.[2] Conveniently aft was sited a pig's ear (urinal), surprisingly (sometimes a real surprise) resembling the voice pipe alongside. This was more or less reserved for the captain, unless one was caught short with no bucket available.

A defence watch, amounting to half the armament, was kept in case of air attack. As the guns had not yet been fired in practice, it was as well that mist rendered us nearly invisible. High alert state damage control was essential because of the mine threat. Meanwhile, the sailors between decks complained incessantly about the horrendous noise of a new device, a pulsating diaphragm designed to activate acoustic mines, and fitted into the ship's side on either side of the stem below the waterline. Fifty years later its hammering would have more than done justice for a rock band.

Suddenly, as we rounded a Channel buoy, there was a violent explosion just off the starboard bow. A mast-high column of brown sea water erupted, the residue landing on the bridge. The ship shuddered. Black smoke poured from the funnels. There was a sinister silence; no boiler room fans, no lights, no generated power and the gyro alarm rang and rang while the compass wandered. Speed dropped to zero. But the acoustic hammer had served its purpose and shortly afterwards the ship was back on course and speed. To activate a mine so close in very shallow water and yet suffer no damage gave everyone much confidence in *Fortune*'s construction and machinery. A single mine had broken the back of *Belfast* and could write off a third of a destroyer's ship's company as well as the ship. There was only one survivor from the cruiser *Neptune* when caught by one off North Africa. *Fortune* had already justified herself eponymously, and there were no more complaints about noise from the messdecks.

Our primitive radar was now coming into its own by detecting a multiplicity of echoes purporting to be of aircraft, ships and land. But there was a snag. All three radar operators, led by Ordinary Seaman Cullen, were Scots with interesting regional accents, which were unintelligible to the management on the bridge. Regional accents were often a barrier before the advent of universal television and radio. When I joined *Vindictive*, manned largely by Londoners, I found cockney incomprehensible. Now the only Scottish officer in *Fortune*, I was constantly required to translate, once even sprinting the length of the ship to do so. With high speed targets this procedure was obviously not the best. Based on a popular comic strip running in *The Daily Sketch*, I allocated PIP for aircraft, SQUEAK for a ship and WILFRED for a land echo. The last emerged from the depths as "WHULFERRUD", but the result was voted a success and lasted the commission. "Pip, Pip, Pip, zero three zero, closing fast. Pip, Pip, Pip."

By now we were many miles behind the voyage plan, due to these and other delays. The most significant effect from my point of view was a lack of navigational lights to fix the ship's position at night. Lighthouses were blacked out in war, as was the country in general. The navigator was expected to order a limited number of lights in crucial positions for the passage stating the period they were needed. This was to avoid helping the enemy. (An obvious precaution, which the U.S. Navy failed to observe when their country entered the war, to their great cost).[3] As our plan had gone awry I was presented with a very dark exercise in coastal Dead Reckoning. All the lights that I had asked for were extinguished by the time we reached them.

My cabin was right aft, just forward of the wardroom. The illogical situation of officers' cabins derived from days of sail, when ships were conned and steered from the poop. This lesson from World War I was hoisted in by the U.S. Navy, but not by the Royal Navy. The tally on the door said boldly in brass "Navigating Officer". "Named" thus, my rights of ownership were, I discovered, fortunately protected by King's Regulations and Admiralty Instructions from envious ship's officers senior to me, such as the lieutenants. At sea, I lived in the box-like chart house under the bridge. The revolution telegraph operating chains passed through it. This arrangement was valuable as I woke instantly when the bridge ordered a rapid change of speed. I slept fully clothed at sea, as we all did.

It was just dusk and I had left the charthouse to go up to the bridge. From here, sliding steel doors each side opened onto sponsons on which were mounted the short-range Oerlikon anti-aircraft guns. The starboard door was open and in the murky twilight through the opening I could see two figures posed like actors on a melodramatic stage.

Crouched on the deck, huddled, white-faced and quivering with fright in his duffle coat, I recognised the captain's steward. Inboard and behind him stood the captain. He was holding a twelve-bore shot gun. I stood aghast as suddenly, without any warning, he raised his gun, aimed it and fired both barrels over the rating's shoulder into the sea.

"Oh, sir," I exclaimed, "why did you do that?"

"What else," he replied, "would you do with a gun-shy dog?"

The steward collapsed and lay in a sobbing heap. I felt sick. Here was my master, whom I wished so much to admire, acting in a cruel and irrational manner, which I found it impossible to justify.

The wretched rating was eventually taken away on a stretcher when we reached harbour, and we never heard of him again. It was said that he suffered from something called paranoia, a condition that I had not heard of at that time. I thought myself that he had been more probably overwhelmed by his imagination and terror of unseen, but lurking, mines and torpedoes. Jack normally concentrated his thoughts on sex or football, which was healthier and safer – or at least they were in those days.

The following day at dusk after an unusually smooth passage of the Pentland Firth and The Minch passing close to the ruined ancestral castle of the Chiefs of Clan Donald, via Cape Wrath, we gave thanks (in my case with undisguised relief) for safe arrival at Macgilligan, the entrance to the River Foyle on which stands the city of Londonderry. With a pilot ordered for the river, I looked forward to a peaceful alongside after a moderately trouble-free maiden passage.

The ship stopped surrounded by inky darkness. Out of the shadows on the neutral Irish shore emerged an unlit skiff, propelled by four oarsmen, strange spectral figures from whom drifted a miasma of Guinness and tobacco smoke.

“It will be you we are looking for. Throw us a line. Not so fast! Here’s your man,” shouted the helmsman.

A lanky shape disentangled and mounted the bridge ladder with difficulty.

"Ach, it's a fine night, captain. How's the war going?" it asked, then vanished. A search around the by now darkened bridge in the vicinity of the binnacle revealed our Southern Irish pilot, stretched out on the gratings, snoring loudly, and well away with the wee fellows in green suits.

Thus began my none too well prepared first passage, assisted by a legless Irishman, up a dimly lit, winding estuary on a pitch dark night. We made it without further incident, which I put down to beginner's luck. I almost forgot to mention another steering failure half way, and subsequent anchoring with no room to swing. Then came the relief beyond belief at the advent of a small unsolicited tug despatched to nurse *Fortune* up to the oiling jetty at Lisahally. Three cheers for this shore staff! The captain, who had been uncharacteristically silent and virtually a spectator during these entertainments, now took the con and surprised everyone by making a perfect alongside in difficult conditions.

I signed the pilot's certificate for his statutory payment with my reservations unexpressed. He would undoubtedly classify me as a stingy Scot for not offering the expected dram to lubricate his bicycle trip across the border after such an admittedly neutral contribution to the war effort. Stripey, the forecastle lockerman, said that his granny from Galway, on

collecting her meagre butter ration, complained, “What was the British Navy doing about them Nasty sobmoreens?”

The next day, topped up with oil, *Fortune* sailed again. The jagged rocks of Innestrahul on the horizon raked the Atlantic storm clouds as she rolled and pitched towards Gibraltar to join Force H. Half the ship’s company was seasick and so was I.

Chapter 4

The Quest

He looked like a man cut away from the stake, when the fire has overrunningly wasted all the limbs without consuming them . . .
Moby Dick, *Herman Melville*

By 1941 book publishers were out of business. This was due not so much to a loss of readers but to shortage of paper, a commodity without which, like ammunition and people, no war can be decently fought. New books were for this reason difficult to come by. Alongside the Admiralty Manuals of Seamanship and Navigation, the shelf in my cabin now supported a limited, but mildly eclectic, mixture of literature in preparation for the unknown future.

Side by side were: *On The Bridge* by Captain J.A.G. Troup, R.N., already mentioned; a collection of Highland Bagpipe music; two or three works by Saki and P.G. Wodehouse, the latter at the time considered unfairly, but understandably, to be a traitor; *The British Blue Jacket 1915-1940*;[1] a biography of Leonardo da Vinci;[2] Mahan's *Influence of Seapower*; Flecker's *Omar Khayyam* and *Moby Dick* by Herman Melville, Everyman edition, the last as yet unopened.

When I was nine I was taken as a treat to a cinema show – silent, black and white with captions. This was Moby Dick[3] and it frightened the life out of me. The action was superb, and I had nightmares for months afterwards – the tortured captain in agony on his back in the boat after his leg was torn off – the stump being cauterised by white-hot harpoon steels. Then later the sinister pegleg searching for a hole drilled specifically for it in the *Pequod*'s deck as its owner struggled with a recalcitrant member of his crew. Apart from being incomprehensible, and grown-ups so often were, the behaviour of the adults depicted in the film compared unfavour-

ably with those in *The Swiss Family Robinson*. Now would be the opportunity, with time on my hands, to get down to the original.

The book itself did take time. Some of it I found difficult, even indigestible, hoisted in at odd moments, in snatches, losing the place, falling asleep. Its allegorical convolutions became puzzles, the import of which would only become apparent much later as I went about different tasks in *Fortune*. Melville's awful Ahab does not emerge on stage in his nineteenth-century New Bedford square-rigged whaler till Chapter 28. Our own captain had made himself invisible till the ship left Sheerness and then spoke to no one unless absolutely necessary. He did not address the ship's company before sailing, nor did he attempt to explain what *Fortune*'s role or future might entail, or what he expected of us. As this story unfolded, I began to wonder whether our own twentieth-century commanding officer, if not quite mad, as Ahab so obviously was, might not be fashioned from a similar mould. He too seemed to be consumed and driven by some terrible inner turmoil. His cruel and irrational treatment of the frightened steward on the first day at sea nagged in my mind.

But there was a significant difference. Ahab's obsessive quest, to find and kill Moby Dick, was evident to all on board from the outset. He made no bones about it. Even the peg leg, replacing the one digested by his submarine adversary, was fashioned from whale bone. His crew was also imbued with his fury of the hunt. There was no need for them to like their captain, nor did they. His skill as a seaman and a killer of whales was their inspiration. What drove *Fortune's* captain, and what tortured him; what fire burned him; or what it was that he sought, was not obvious – at least it was not to me at the time. But his rough and arrogant treatment of officers and ratings was very much so. I wondered what on earth could be the matter with the man, but kept this to myself.

Chapter 5

Who Did That?

. . . Soothly in any tretis of the Astrolabe, that I have seyn, there ben some conclusions that wole not in alle things performen hir behestes; and some hem ben too harde to thy tendre age of ten to conseyve.

Chaucer

Could it be wild thyme and jonquils? The heady scent of Gibraltar wafted on the wind called Levanter met us off Cape St. Vincent. It had been an unexpectedly quiet passage from Londonderry across the Bay of Biscay and U-boat deployment route, picking up the distant loom of Spanish and Portuguese lighthouses. *Fortune* was soon one of many destroyers berthed together, an organised, but apparently higglety-pigglety, huddle of masts, flags, funnels, guns and activity in the appropriately named pens at the north end of Gibraltar harbour.

Our arrival on 7th December coincided with the devastating news of the Japanese attack on Pearl Harbour, which brought the United States into the war. We were now, although fighting Japan, Germany and Italy, no longer all alone. It was

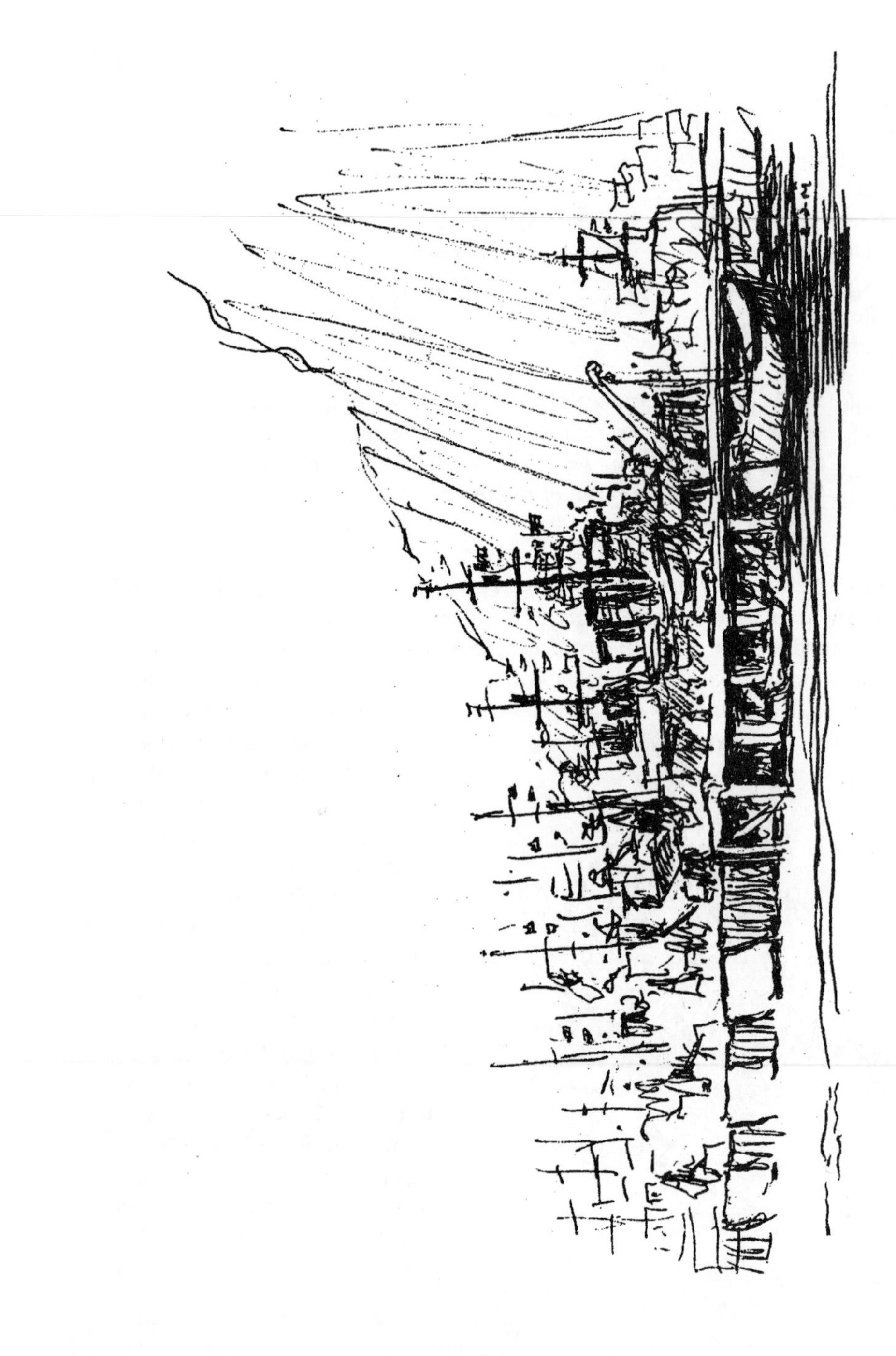

easier to feel sure of success with America at last openly an ally. Soviet Russia seemed an enigma by reason of her devious prewar treaty with Hitler and because of Stalin's awful track record. In spite of this there were those sufficiently misguided to sanctify him as "Uncle Joe", but not in the Navy.[1]

Fortune was scarcely the happiest ship in Force H. The officers got on well with each other in spite of, or perhaps because of, their different backgrounds. Odd man out was the ultra-serious young R.N.V.R. surgeon lieutenant. "Sea legs" eluded him and, unusually for a ship's doctor, he kept himself to himself, which was a serious loss. Not many officers could contribute as much to a destroyer's well being in war than an entertaining and civilised doctor. The chief and petty officers pulled their weight in a detached sort of way. The more technical their expertise the less their immediate dependence on the whims of their master, provided of course that his bath water was hot. Sailors have traditionally created an art form, usually humorous, out of grumbling. Ours complained, but without many jokes. Jack would not have much enjoyed being alternately ignored and then the target of abuse. He had already tired of what initially provided entertainment when his officers were at the receiving end.

I tried to avoid the conclusion, a sort of blasphemy for a very junior officer with a vocation, that it was our C.O.'s unpredictability and saturnine temperament which made his ship less than comfortable. Other destroyers, berthed alongside, doubtless had their own problems, but they were so evidently a high-spirited lot, with up-beat and competent good leaders in command. Anyway that was how it looked from our side of the hedge. Yet I hoped against hope that when he settled in things would improve. The standard "Salt Horse", driving – the current expression – his destroyer was a professional. Experienced and knowledgeable, he might drink like a proverbial fish in harbour, where "Jimmy" (the First Lieutenant) took over running the ship, as some did; but at sea he was magnificent. There, with the cork firmly in the bottle, he drove himself as well as his ship to, and well beyond, her limits. Some killed themselves in the process. Admiral Cunningham was a World War I "salt horse" destroyer "driver".[2] Our master aimed to conform with the harbour performance. It remained to be seen whether he would meet the high standard required at sea.

We had begun to avoid him, which in practice was not always easy in such a small ship. In harbour he ate most meals in the wardroom, normal procedure for a lieutenant commander-in-command. It was the custom to

wait until he appeared before sitting down to lunch or dinner. He was rarely punctual. He had no conversation or small talk and sat gloomily and silent at the head of the table. In *Moby Dick* I had reached the passage describing the awful captain's silent dining table where "Ahab presided like a mute, maned sea-lion on the white coral beach, surrounded by his warlike but still deferential cubs."

What was to prove a very short stint with Force H incorporated a hotch potch of events. The captain called quite correctly on Captain (D) 19 (flotilla commander) in the leader, *Laforey*.[3] I deduced from his defensive attitude on return, as obviously did others, that this confrontation had not been a great success. Yet there was some relief, if only temporary. It was provided by Lt. commander Bill Beloe,[4] himself a professional destroyer man, at the time serving in the battleship *Malaya* in company. His presence in a big ship was said to have been due to a recent navigational argument between his previous command and the Mersey Light Vessel. An officer of charm and ability, he had been a contemporary of our C.O. as a cadet at the Royal Naval College. The hospitality and kindness that he offered was beneficial and percolated through to us.

Number One had his wits about him when, returning to the dockyard one evening from a Christmas shopping expedition in Main Street, he was stopped by two large Liverpool Irish stokers from another ship. Caps flat-aback and balancing themselves upright with difficulty and some mutual support, they had evidently enjoyed a successful run ashore. Both expressed a distaste for R.N. executive officers in general and Michael Morris, whom they had never met before, in particular. No one else was in sight. A small moon glimmered above the blacked-out street. Number One suspected that he was in for a difficult time, but he had not been the Mate of a merchant ship for nothing.

"You are members of your ship's heroic engine room department," he began, laying it on thick. They agreed.

"You must therefore be experts in the vital subject of Damage Control." They said that of course they were, so what?

"If I ask you a question on a damage control subject, and you don't know the answer, will you promise to let me go on my way?"

"By Jasus, on our mithers' 'onnor, sorr."

"Then tell me all you know about the Ashwell System?"

They scratched their heads, gazed at each other, hiccoughed, and then reluctantly admitted that they were stumped. Honour satisfied, Number One was allowed to proceed with dignity. On return to their ship, if they remembered the occasion, the stokers would have discovered that "The Ashwell System" was the legend inscribed on the inside of the ratchet-controlled brass lock on the door of an officers' heads (lavatory). It was a device unlikely ever to be seen by a stoker, unless he was the plumber's mate. Doors, "Heads" for the use of, in those far-off days were supplied for officers only.[5]

We were entertained by a visit from Admiral Sir James Somerville, commanding Force H, an officer of personality and style, whom I remembered well from my time in *Valiant*. Lower deck was cleared for him to address the ship's company. He joked about the quality of sooty smuts deposited by the wardroom galley funnel onto his white cap cover. He explained with sincerity the effect on the strength of Force H of the addition of even one destroyer. He mentioned the difficulty he had in

coming to grips with the Italians as their fleet always ran away.[6] This, he added, did not apply to their midget submarines or, as we were to discover, to their torpedo bombers.

He described how, when dressed in khaki shorts and shirt with only his uniform cap to indicate rank, during a walk on the top of the Rock he had chatted up a Black Watch sentry. Feeling that sentries ought to salute passing admirals, he pointed to his cap – two rows of gold oak leaves – and asked, "Do you know what rank I am?" "Weel, sir, ye may be a serrgeant majorr, but I ken yerr no in the Black Watch." Hearts rose. We had been sent an example in leadership. His act was so like that of a genial country

squire that it would have surprised nobody had he handed out a brace of pheasants to the gangway staff on going down the ladder to his barge.

In his unlaced galley boots the scruffy little wardroom cook,[7] "Sooty" from now on, felt that his personal problem had been recognised by high authority even though he was now required to sweep the "Charley Noble" (galley chimney) six times a day. Somehow I felt sure that the strained atmosphere in the ship could not have escaped the great man's attention, but he would probably have attributed it to genuine growing pains in a newly commissioned, and unworked-up, ship. This incidently was the only visit by any flag officer to *Fortune* throughout. Nor for that matter can I recall one by any administrative authority.[8]

During this period we carried out a patrol in the Straits of Gibraltar, followed by a relatively uneventful foray eastwards into the Mediterranean with Force H, during which the old aircraft carrier *Argus*, a floating box, flew off fighters to reinforce Malta. Some individual gunnery firing exercises in idyllic weather, under the stunning violet mountains of Andalucia were designed to improve efficiency. Shooting at barely moving air and surface towed targets was rudimentary and without any specialist supervision. Each event culminated in a circus rather than a candid assessment of mistakes. It was a do-it-yourself, very amateur work-up, and by any standard inadequate to meet the diverse threats posed

by dedicated enemies. The one outstanding achievement was not to lose the torpedo that we fired, thus avoiding an official "displeasure".

I spent two uneventful, but lumpy, nights on duty armed with hand grenades in a picket boat patrolling the harbour entrance, on the lookout for Italian naval manned torpedoes. The riders, known as Charioteers, would have their heads above water to see where they were going. These missiles were from time to time loosed off from the submerged compartment of their mother ship berthed across the bay in neutral Spanish Algeciras. Curiously it was still possible for a British officer to have dinner at the Hotel Reina Cristina, the other side of the street from this hostile submarine garage, provided he could afford the bill, which I could not as a sublieutenant. Like most of my contemporaries, I lived on my pay. Nevertheless, Spanish neutrality with Franco-style limitations was better than active hostility.

A voluntary all night patrol in an R.A.F. Sunderland flying boat was more interesting, but frigid because there was no heating and I had no flying kit. My predecessor on a flight from the U.K. had been the Foreign Secretary, Anthony Eden. The pilot told me that he was surprised by the sight of such a sartorially elegant figure transiting towards the "heads" in long johns. I paid for my keep by identifying a suspicious darkened surface target as one of our own destroyers. The air crew digested about a

month's civilian sweet ration during the flight. Later, an anti-submarine patrol in the much superior American-built long range Catalina flying boat was disappointingly cancelled at the last moment.

Diversions included a wardroom run ashore to the impoverished and at that time pathetic Spanish border town of La Linea with the picturesque, as seen from the distance, hill-top bull ring of San Rocco, where in former days Jack cheered the bull. Fino Sherry, but few tappas, sampled in different bars, followed an "out of working hours" (and therefore surprise to the ladies), reconnaissance of a brothel. Madam appeared rubbing her eyes with apologies for the national siesta and promised a variety of unusual diversions. We escaped leaving a small donation to compensate for an ungentlemanly disturbance.

The C.O. arranged for an ENSA troupe (officially sponsored entertainers visiting the Rock's garrison), including a couple of not unattractive ladies, to be given tea in the wardroom. Although well intentioned, this back-fired. The sailors resented that officers appeared to be hogging assets primarily intended for Jack, Tommy and Jock. They were right.

The written word of higher authority was evidently all important to the captain, which of course is perfectly proper. Conforming with regulations, which stipulated compulsory Sunday worship, the captain, when taking the service on the upper deck, failed to detect a lack of amendment in the time-worn naval issue prayer book, and prayed loudly and confidently by name for a glorious, but long gone, monarch. Then realising his mistake

and without pausing to draw breath, he shouted, "Who the hell has forgotten to amend this bloody book?" Jack enjoyed this.[9]

In January *Fortune* escorted a Norwegian oil tanker *Leif Ericson* to a position south of Madeira, then rendezvoused with another, *Glendal*, and brought her back with her precious cargo essential to Force H's operations. Several attacks with depth charges were made on contacts classified as "possible submarine" with no apparent result except for a shoal of dead fish, which for obvious reasons it was too risky to stop to pick up, and whose echoes had set up the "possible submarine" contact.

Our Anti-submarine expertise depended entirely on the skill of the H.S.D. (senior Asdic petty officer), sensible, careful Leading Seaman Clark. Poor Mathews, the nominally responsible officer, through no fault of his own knew little of this technique and nothing of the tactics. This was the Navy's fault.[10] He worried hopelessly, frightened by the antics and agitations of the captain, who put on an act but was evidently equally

unsure. Work-up training in anti-submarine warfare had been non-existent. The ship's capability was therefore embarrassingly amateur. At the time I thought – mistakenly as I found out later – that a single escort would not have been of any consequence, except possibly to deter a "makee-learn" U-boat. Nevertheless, *Fortune* had now twice fulfilled the classic aim of "safe and timely arrival" of a convoy. In her previous commission under different management[11] and with a sister ship, *Forester*, she had sunk U-27 and captured its crew.

I was distressed by the time, and lots of mistakes, that it took me to resolve navigational star sights by the laborious system that we had been taught using logarithms. Adding up columns of figures with the ship rolling her guts out was not my forte, not like my father, who could beat a Chinese clerk with mental arithmetic in spite of the other's abacus. There had to be a quicker method requiring no perception of the intricacies of spherical trignometry. The captain suggested that I might ask the R.A.F. how it found out where it was. Obviously they had to know where they had been before they arrived. In exchange for a bottle of duty free gin, I acquired from my friendly Sunderland's navigator the relevant "light blue" tables and air almanac. An Admiralty label warned "not to be used except by specialist navigating officers", to which I turned a blind eye, though I admired the picture on the cover of an early navigator peering through his backstaff above the motto "Man is not lost". This serendipitous discovery stood me in good stead, and I was grateful for the captain's suggestion. Years later a similar process was adopted by the Navy.

It enabled the position based on a number of stars to be worked out and plotted at speed. On the other hand, an Air Force plotting device, that the C.O. was sold on, turned out to be useless for a ship, so I hid it in the bottom locker. He himself never once took a sun or star sight, and admitted that he could not see a thing through a sextant. I now began to delight in identifying and making use of the stars I caught in the telescope as they scudded in and out of clouds at dusk and dawn.

I seemed to have become somehow the ship's operations officer although in those days such a post was not specifically identified. Being responsible for navigation and signals, I had to know in advance about what was on the cards, in order to prepare charts and plans and to make certain that watch was set on the right radio circuits. This advanced knowledge was a touchy subject when it concerned the activity of battleships and aircraft carriers, which could be vulnerable targets for a U-boat when committed to a steady course as they emerged from Gibraltar harbour towards the open sea.

The C.O. and Number One were now barely on speaking terms. Obsessive about security, essential information about the ship's future, which his second in command needed to know to be able to stock the ship with the appropriate stores, victuals and ammunition, was sometimes not divulged by the captain until the last minute. Responsibility for passing the word became mine by default, with the added complication that I was supposed for some reason to keep such information to myself. Had Number One not been a thoughtful and generous personality, my position would have been intolerable.

It has been standard practice since long before Nelson's day for admirals to complain about a shortage of frigates. The only difference in World War II was for "frigate" read "destroyer". Pressure was applied to extract ships from adjacent commands by hook or by crook. Being modest about our general capability, nobody onboard was the least surprised when the next offering volunteered by Flag Officer Force H to reinforce the Mediterranean Fleet based in Alexandria turned out to be *Fortune*. What did surprise was the lack of notice given for our departure. We would never know whether the captain had sat on the information. I pushed *Vanity Fair* borrowed from the Garrison Library into the signal tower, and got a reminder two months later.

Force H sailed after dark on 9th February 1942. Course was to be set initially westward. Atlantic convoys first set out to the East. This gambit was supposed to confuse unfriendly observers in Spain. The Force would then turn and head back through the straits of Gibraltar. The brand-new 5.25 inch gun cruiser *Cleopatra*, with *Fortune*, would at a pre-arranged time be detached independently to Malta and thence to Alexandria. The destroyer screen was required to sail first. *Fortune* would need to make a sternboard from her berth, turn in the harbour and then proceed out through the breakwater entrance. Order of sailing was, as usual, strictly timed with minimum space between each unit's movement.

The captain returned from shore at the last minute. He must have fortified himself for the occasion. This was one emergency that I had not prepared for. I approached Number One, and suggested that he should take the ship out of harbour as, in my view, the captain was incapable. At the time I supposed that, because of their tricky relationship, Number One insisted, as I was navigator, this was logically my "part of ship and the best of British luck, Sub." In hindsight I can see that the First Lieutenant's difficulty was that the captain was undeniably still physically upright and in his own opinion able to take the ship to sea. His second in command would have needed to persuade him that he was unwell. This involved the doctor, who would have confirmed his good health, which was not in dispute. Dealing with a sozzled C.O. was unlikely to have figured in a Reserve officer's preparation for the Royal Navy.

Time came for *Fortune* to cast off. As a midshipman I had run the usual picket boats and a forty-five-foot launch in all sorts of places and weather. Also I had had the unusual experience (luck) for a cadet of handling a single screw steam drifter, taking liberty men to and from the fleet in Scapa Flow and Loch Ewe. But to manoeuvre a destroyer, for the first time ever, out of Gibraltar harbour in an organised fleet movement with ships darkened and no harbour or leading marks was a bit of a jump.

There was no time to consider the implications. The captain was dimly visible hunched on the bridge wing. I stood nervously amidships at the voice pipe that communicated with the coxswain in the wheel house. The standard orders to ring on and obey telegraphs were passed. Those referring to letting go berthing wires forward and aft were routine. Then, from the C.O., emerged a series of instructions for wheel and engine movements, several of which seemed to me to be somewhat confused and inappropriate. I repeated aloud each of his commands, meanwhile keeping my hand firmly over the mouth of the voice pipe. Then discreetly, and not without anxiety, I transmitted an edited version down to the Coxswain, at the same time turning a deaf ear to his repeated, "Speak up sir, please."

Somehow or other, *Fortune* stumbled at the right moment through the gap between the Detached Mole and the South breakwater into Algeciras Bay and took up her allotted station on the spread out anti-submarine screen. Only later it occurred to me that, had a collision or grounding been the outcome, the accused at the subsequent court martial would have been the insubordinate junior officer, who had so flagrantly disobeyed his superior's orders. Much later, I did enjoy a discreet pat on the back from the First Lieutenant.

The screening destroyers were now in position. The big ships emerged and altered course westward towards the Atlantic. All went like clockwork, secretly and in silence. Then, just as the Force had been turned through 180 degrees to point at the entrance to the Mediterranean, pitch black night was turned into day. A "Snowflake" rocket had exploded overhead and illuminated all. Spies in Spain agitated their Morse keys to Berlin. Horrified, I realised that *Fortune* was responsible. The young seaman gunner, Fitzgerald, whose job it was to set up a device, specifically designed for illuminating surfaced U-boats in a convoy action, had accidentally fired it.

"Who did that?" flashed the flagship.[12] There was an uneasy silence on the bridge.

"I think we had better own up, sir. It will come out in the long run."

"Hell and damnation!"

To *Fortune* from Flag Officer commanding Force H:

"Negative Duff George," (manoeuvre not well executed).

Chapter 6

Russian Roulette

The grand object of travelling is to see the shores of the Mediterranean.

Dr. Samuel Johnson

Terribly upset with her own performance, *Fortune* made herself discreet on the screen of Force H heading east on 9th February 1942. The aim of the exercise was a sweep into the Mediterranean during which the brand new 5.25-inch calibre gun cruiser *Cleopatra*, Captain Matthew Slattery,[1] and *Fortune* would be detached to join the Mediterranean Fleet in Alexandria, stopping at Malta on the way. *Argus* had, in our last foray with Force H, flown off replacements to reinforce the air defence of Malta, which at the time consisted of a few elderly fighters, worthy successors to three ex-naval Gladiators, Faith, Hope and Charity, which originally were the only air defence. Malta was the pivot of the war in the theatre. Although its defence was immensely costly in ships and lives, no one could possibly question the validity of this policy, and certainly the enemy did not, since the loss of the island would have sealed the fate of the British Desert Army and thus the Middle East.[2]

In support of this *Fortune* had embarked a deck cargo of aero-engines and spare parts, which filled the iron deck on both sides from the bridge superstructure to the torpedo tubes. This, together with extra 4.7-inch ammunition stacked round the guns, created a substantial increase in top weight and thus a reduction in stability. It also offered a challenging obstacle race. Going from forward to aft, the upper deck was the only route in prewar destroyers owing to total subdivision of the hull by watertight bulkheads. At times, heavy seas made this journey impassable even with man-ropes rigged. An officer of the watch sometimes had to

wait on the bridge until the weather moderated sufficiently to allow a successor to fight his way up. Artificers and stokers were equally tested in reaching the engineroom hatches.

The plan was to detach *Cleopatra* with *Fortune* in time to cross the gap from Cape Bon to Malta in the dark hours of 10th/11th February. This narrow patch of sea was so close to enemy airfields in Sicily that, without air cover, life for ships spending any time there could be brutish and sometimes short. In the event, due to delays caused by winds adverse for flying and a series of alarming, though unsuccessful, bombing runs by the Luftwaffe, our two-ship unit was obliged to run the gauntlet in broad daylight on the 11th. As we left Force H the destroyer *Anthony* made a signal to *Cleopatra*: "Don't we have a rendezvous tonight?" To which the remarkable reply was, "Your signal not understood."

There was a stiff westerly wind, a clear blue sky and a long following sea. With little warning from radar a series of JU 88s, twin-engined German bombers, appeared from out of the sun and elsewhere. They attacked in pairs, in a shallow dive to about 500 feet over the sea.

Continuously at Action Stations, all four 4.7-inch guns, with a maximum elevation of only thirty-five degrees, fired away as did the two bridge Oerlikons and the 3-inch A.A. gun. The noise must have been terrific. But one did not hear it simply because it was sweet music to the ears. Only the frenetic shouts of the captain, aimed upwards and backwards at the First Lieutenant in the director control tower, penetrated whenever there was a momentary interlude in the fusillade. None of us wore tin hats or ear defenders, and anti-flash gear was not yet with us, but we did sport inflatable life belts tied round our middles; not too low to avoid floating feet up.

Meanwhile, I stood with the captain on the bridge, between us keeping the ship under continuous wheel. As she was at full power – "The white-hot wake the "wildering speed" and well over thirty knots – the erratic manoeuvres would have been unhelpful for even a sophisticated gunnery system. *Fortune*'s not being in that category, the guns' crews made up in quantity and enthusiasm for anything lacking in quality. Judging by the huge splashes and thuds from near misses all round, the opposition seemed to find its target elusive. Luck seemed to be on our side.

As the first bombs burst close by, I found myself instinctively down on the wooden deck gratings, with the captain alongside. He was horizontal, as was everyone else, while the ship roared under maximum wheel at full power. We both got up. It was embarrassing. Obviously, however one felt, it was important to appear imperturbable. Besides, neither the fragile bridge screen nor the deck were designed to offer the slightest bodily protection even against splinters. During subsequent attacks I held confidentially onto "Lord Kelvin's balls", the nicely named compass correctors which, with Flinder's bar, bestrode the binnacle. This support helped to avoid staggering under the ship's violent motion, created by a combination of heavy wheel, high speed and a following sea. It occurred to me that no one had ever been so undignified as to "hit the deck" on *Valiant's* bridge in similar circumstances.

The captain presumably went through a similar thought process, although he said nothing about it either then or later. It was even more important to stand up for practical reasons such as to see out and so avoid collision with the much larger *Cleopatra*, who was charging about in much the same way and rather too close for comfort. Meanwhile, it was important to keep a weather eye open for the next hostile onslaught. The whole performance was more interesting than Russian roulette, but lacked that pastime's finesse. *Fortune's* heraldic wheel and wing were evidently spinning satisfactorily so far.

Much fuel and ammunition had now been expended. This loss in displacement added to the top-heavy effect produced by the deck cargo. Unlike the U.S.N. the R.N. did not compensate for stability by flooding empty fuel tanks from the sea. The ship became increasingly and obviously unstable, rather like driving a car on ice. Turning one way and then the other, driven hard she lay over almost to the guard rails and was sluggish in coming upright in between. Committed to the shortest course for Malta, when not taking avoiding action, with full speed rung on and surrounded by a heavy following sea, the rudder became less and less effective. Control could only be regained temporarily by a short sharp reduction in revolutions in order to maintain some relative movement between sea and rudder. Conditions in the engine, boiler room and magazines were even more unattractive than the bridge, where we did at least have the advantage of appreciating the scenery, together with any amount of fresh air, even if laced with funnel fumes driven past by the wind.

The inevitable occurred. One minute she was planing like a speed boat on the crest of a wave, the next she appeared to slide back down hill. *Fortune* broached to in the classic manner of a three-masted, square-rigged ship. Turning entirely out of control at right angles to the sea, she lay over on her starboard side, with the gunwale and deck edge well under water. I hung on to my friendly binnacle until it was almost horizontal. Then, letting go, I dropped down onto the previously vertical torpedo control instrument box mounted on the side of the bridge, fortunately built to robust Admiralty specification.

The tops of both funnels now lay just above the waves, billowing black smoke. The ship was well beyond her designer's predicted vanishing angle. Two more bombs exploded alongside. I felt sure that she was about to capsize and wondered with some interest what the effect the sea would have when it went down the funnels. Time stood still. It was probably only a minute or so. Imperceptibly at first, then, very slowly, the ship gradually came upright with gyro alarm-bell ringing and the boiler-room fans, a destroyer's roaring lungs, dying to an eerie silence.

The guns continued to bang away. Sailors are adept at improvisation. Terrible Petty Officer Jacko, captain of 'B' gun, boasted that a 4.7 shell had loaded itself downwards by gravity off the tray. His more modest opposite number at 'A' gun claimed to have fired at 90 degrees elevation, 55 degrees beyond the gun's limits, when the ship was on her beam ends.

It speaks volumes for her design, construction and ship's company that *Fortune* gradually gathered speed and was soon under way again at full power. Amazingly there were no casualties or any damage other than bent

guard rails, davits and stove-in boat. Sooty's galley was in chaos. The vital deck cargo, well lashed down and covered, was wet but intact. The Luftwaffe would have been justified in claiming an Iron Cross having sighted the port bilge keel, and much of the red anti-foul painted bottom, together with one large bronze propeller rotating above the waves.

Cleopatra, with her ability to go faster in these conditions, signalled helpfully to ask if we required her to stand by till we reached Malta, otherwise she would go on ahead independently. The captain immediately turned to me and asked, "Sub, can you guarantee to find the end of the swept channel?" This would take us safely through the unmarked defen-

sive minefield that protected Grand Harbour. Under normal circumstances I would have indignantly replied, "Yes, of course, sir." But the gyro compass had toppled. The magnetic compass was "boxing" itself. I actually did know in theory how to fix a position using a horizontal sextant, which would have been the solution without a compass. It needs a steady hand. An instant decision was called for. I admitted, albeit reluctantly, to being not over-confident about providing the pinpoint pilotage required to locate the entrance to an unmarked swept channel through a known minefield in the present circumstances. If *Cleopatra* would stay in company, "I really would be much happier, Sir, although of course I can always have a shot at it." He was obviously only too happy to accept this and did not question my reasons. In retrospect, it is extraordinary that a Lt. Commander in command should have relied totally on an acting Sub-lieutenant for a tricky navigational opinion with possibly awful consequences.

Everyone on the bridge was puffing cigarettes to steady nerves and hands, an unprofitable exercise for me, being a non-smoker. Broaching to quite spoils the day, as someone, possibly Thucydides, once said about a collision. On the other hand, provided they miss, bombs are soon forgotten.

Cleopatra did stay in company and subsequently took a direct hit. Seven sailors and the Master-at-Arms were killed and also Sublieutenant

Roy Walmsley,[3] who had been my contemporary in the training cruiser *Vindictive*. I have not forgotten my part in this decision and its consequence. Did I funk it? I suppose I could justify lack of navigational confidence in retrospect by the belief that it would have been a greater catastrophe had *Fortune* missed the channel and run onto a "friendly" minefield. Several ships did soon after, with much loss of life.

The captain accumulated some credit with the ship's company for skill in dodging bombs.

Chapter 7

You Can't Win

The boy stood on the burning deck
Whence all but he had fled . . .
Casabianca, Felicia Hemans

On 11th February 1942 a battered but thankful *Fortune* berthed alongside in French Creek, which leads off Grand Harbour, Valetta. It is narrow and was at the time cluttered with a variety of dockyard craft and at least one wreck. Above rose Senglea, a multitude of lemon and ochre stone houses – square patterns throwing violet shadows across biscuit-coloured rock.

A chorus of Maltese dockyard workmen, Borgs, Caruanas, Mifsuds and Debonos, scrambled over the guard rails to remove our vital deck cargo of aero engines and to survey damage. We were touched and impressed by this reception (though of course no brass band playing "Roll out the Barrel", as I remembered on the occasion of *Valiant's* spectacular arrival in 1940). A clatter of hammers and riveting was music to our ears, as it advertised that work had already started. The infinitesimal delay between berthing and start of work must have created a world record for speed of dockyard reaction.[1]

As the youngest, it was logical that the duties of Officer of the Day on the first night in harbour should fall to the Sublieutenant. Dusk fell and lights went out. The wardroom and ship's company departed gratefully for the shelter of caverns in the rock, formerly mediaeval magazines, to spend a well-earned quiet night. The "Duty Part of the Watch" of about twelve seamen and stokers remained on board as damage control and fire party. Our ship's armament was unsuitable for urban anti-aircraft defence. When he went over the side Number One waved to me, as always, cheerfully.

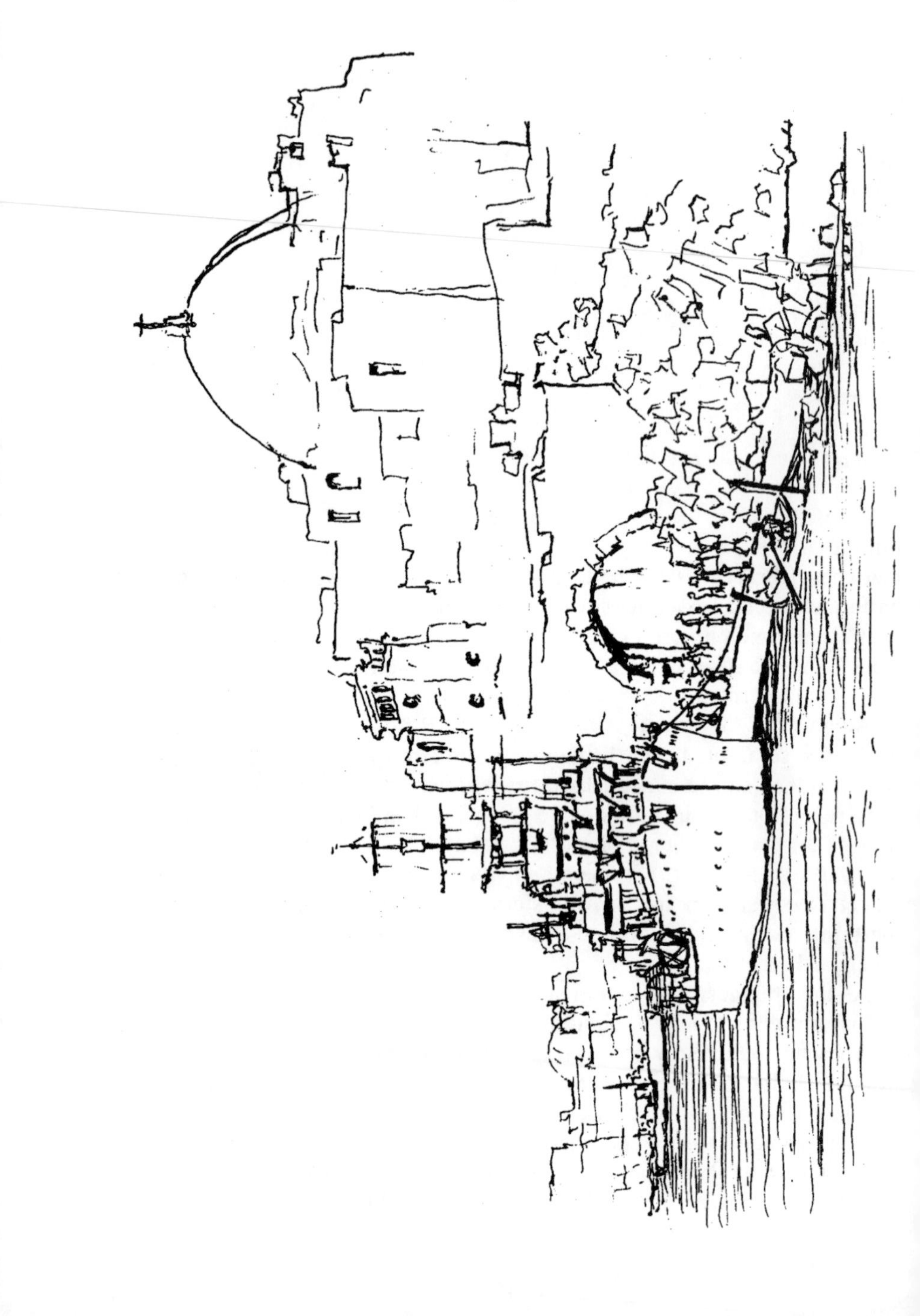

"Keep her steady, Sub. I'm off to the dungeons. Mustn't burn out before reaching flag rank."

There was no moon. I could make out silhouettes of Renaissance domes and ivory battlements against a velvet starlit sky. It was immensely peaceful and silent. The ghost of Jean de la Valette, Grand Master of the Knights of St. John on the ramparts of Fort St. Angelo, where now flew a St. George's Cross, grumbled that he thought he had dealt with sieges once and for all nearly 400 years before.

Shortly after midnight the captain, who had been hospitably entertained by the army garrison mess, returned in good order, grunted "off to bed" and went down to his cabin. He could not have fitted in much, if any, sleep or rest since leaving Gibraltar. I knew, because I was in the same boat. Doctors in the fleet had been pushing officially a drug called Benzedrine to keep you awake in operational extremis. I did not use it, but whether the captain had I do not know.

Suddenly, at about two in the morning, I heard the characteristic intermittent drone of Heinkel engines overhead. Searchlights stabbed the blackness and lit up Valetta from Floriana to the Barracca. Anti-aircraft batteries banged away furiously. The night sky was spectacular with fiery

bursts. A stick of high explosive flashed and erupted among the buildings of nearby, densely populated Cospicua and Vittoriosa. Before I could decide what to do next, the duty destroyer, *Maori*, whose dark shape I could just make out lying on a slip rope in Grand Harbour, blew up with a tremendous bang as the result of a direct hit. This was followed by fire. Flames rapidly spread across the surface of the harbour.

Matters got worse. A slight northerly breeze stirred the water. This pushed burning oil fuel from the sinking destroyer up the creek towards us. The Captain's Night Order Book stated succinctly (and traditionally), "Call me if in doubt." Doubt was by now an understatement of my appreciation of a rapidly deteriorating situation.

I ran down the ladder, went into his cabin and called him. There was no reply.

"Sir," I said, at the top of my voice, "you must come on deck."

I described with some immediacy a "wall of flame" advancing inexorably towards his ship. Silence. Eventually I heard a grunt and something which sounded like, "Some funny story, Sub."

I hurried back to the upper deck. As the creek narrowed the flames were not only getting closer but higher. The ship's engines were now at several hours notice for steam. It would take at least ten minutes to get anybody back from the caverns. Letting go all berthing wires was obviously not a solution, the creek being a cul-de-sac. I hurried down to the captain's cabin once more.

"Captain, Sir, there really is a huge wall of flame. It's now only about a hundred yards astern. You must come up at once."

Total silence.

I repeated the message, using my "gale over the forecastle" voice with volume control turned up to naval parade ground intensity. At last from a mound of blanket on the bunk came a positive instruction: "Bugger off!"

By now the flames were much closer. The Duty Part of sailors mustered all available fire fighting equipment, comprising two hoses, some primitive extinguishers and a bucket of sand. We squirted liquid hopefully over the stern. The Leading Seaman commented drily that it was now so hot he could smell his beard singe. I wondered what would happen next. None of this promised well for the immediate future. Protective clothing did not exist. Any amount of cordite, fireworks, calcium flares and other explosives were stacked generously around in Ready Use lockers, together with the ship's outfit of depth charges. Rarely have I felt more useless.

Then, just when all appeared lost, like the Spanish Armada, came a miracle. The wind backed through 180 degrees. The flames, which licked

the stern, now receded down the creek towards Grand Harbour. But, horrors, peering over the guard rails I could see that all the paintwork and the pendant numbers H 70 were blistered, peeling and a sickly yellow.

"Right," I said, "out stages, scrape and paint. Slap it on quick, lads. Do your best. Make and Mend tomorrow."

This performance might appear out of context, or even eccentric, in the circumstances to someone unacquainted with the ways of the Royal Navy. What remained of the night was relatively uneventful, only a desultory bomb or two with bangs and flashes in more distant parts of the island. Darkened ambulances moved about. Ships' boats and dghaisas were busy in the distance around the spot where *Maori* had once been.

On the dot at seven o'clock the captain went ashore and began his routine constitutional, a brisk walk up and down the jetty with arms behind his back and head bent forward. He frowned meanwhile as he ruminated over the responsibilities of command, or so I presumed. Suddenly, after three perambulations, he stopped in his tracks with a jerk, and stood bolt upright.

"Sub," he exclaimed, pointing, his arm outstretched, "Sub, what the hell has happened to the back end of the ship?"

I went through the, by now, only too familiar routine, "wall of flame" and so on, adding, for good measure, an apology for the somewhat slapdash brushwork round the pendant numbers.

"For God's sake, why on earth didn't you call me?"

Chapter 8

The Guest Night

In this act 'mutiny' means a combination between two or more persons subject to service laws to disobey such authority in such circumstances as to make the disobedience subversive of discipline.

Naval Discipline Act (abbreviated)[1]

Fortune's arrival at bustling, tannery-pungent Alexandria, – visible to seaward only by the Great Pass beacon and Ras el Tin lighthouse, neither as impressive as Pharos of antiquity – coincided with the abject surrender of Singapore on 15th February. I remember this disaster as the nadir of the war. The dramatic loss of the elderly, unarmoured battle cruiser *Repulse* and brand new battleship *Prince of Wales*, apparently committed to an operation which was suicidal without air cover, advertised the basic weakness and obsolescence of the British Fleet in comparison with the Imperial Japanese Navy.

The outlook was not inviting. We knew little of the circumstances of the military debacle at Singapore, except that the fixed defences apparently pointed the wrong way, although there was no shortage of rumours. In the event, these strange stories proved to be less lurid and less unpalatable than the truth. The world-wide Empire, on which we had been brought up, and which had coloured so much of my school atlas red, looked very shaky indeed. Loss of face in the Far East, a particularly oriental phenomenon I knew only too well, would be spectacular and lasting. Our backs were obviously very much against the wall.

The passage from Malta, as part of an escort and covering force consisting of fire cruisers and twenty-three destroyers and three submarines for a convoy of four empty merchantmen, had been uneventful except for showers of bombs delivered mainly by JU 88s, fortunately all unsuccessful. My sight book records feebly on 14th February as an excuse for unfinished calculation, "too much bombing". It occurred to me that German Air Force pilots were not so good as Japanese naval aviators.

Having prepared for the next event to be a "spud run" to Tobruk, where the beleaguered army was kept in provisions and ammunition by a series of nightly destroyer trips – unattractive and unpopular – we were unexpectedly ordered to collect a Top Secret chart of Port T. The code name turned out to be Addu Atoll in the Maldive Islands, a place in the Indian Ocean that none of us had heard of before. Every man Jack was employed embarking ammunition, fuel and stores at the rush. The motor boat was still under repair. There was no sign of the once prolific Alexandrine water taxis, pretty lateen-rigged white feluccas each with a huge and barefooted, nightshirt-clad helmsman, who politely offered his fare the tiller. Instead, sailing the whaler single-handed inshore to the Admiralty chart

depot was a nostalgic diversion along the route that, as a midshipman, I used to steer a launch containing 100 well-oiled and vociferous liberty men back to *Valiant* from Number Six Gate.

On route I had to deliver some official correspondence to the destroyer depot ship *Woolwich*. While onboard I was surprised to be told that the Rear Admiral (Destroyers) wanted to see me. I was suitably impressed by the friendly, tough-looking Rear Admiral Irvine Glenny, wearing open-necked tropical rig and seated behind a massive desk impressively clear of paper. He was the first admiral that had ever spoken to me. I seem to remember that he asked how things were and that I replied, "Fine, sir", lying through my teeth. Fortunately there were no searching questions. Afterwards, I wondered what his reaction would have been had I replied, "Sir, my captain is a nutcase."

Alexandria, with its Sporting Club swimming pool, decorated by nubile young girls, (including pre-teenager, Claudie, later to appear in *Bitter Lemons*),[2] its rugger field and golf course, had been a paradise for Mediterranean Fleet midshipmen in short intervals between active operations only the year before. The international community were generously hospi-

table. A Swiss family with three pretty daughters had entertained us. I was swept off my feet by shy teenage Marguerite, but lacked confidence to do anything about it. Some years after the war I met her quite by chance. She told me that she had felt the same – a very tactful lady.

But there was no opportunity for fun now. *Fortune* was ordered to sail immediately and independently to join the newly formed Eastern Fleet, which we assumed correctly was somewhere in the vicinity of Addu Atoll. The ship's company felt, not without reason, that nothing could be worse than staying in the Mediterranean, whose shores they had not seen, and did not now want to see. I had last passed through Port Said in the Blue Funnel steamer, *Antenor*,[3] when I was five. My mother bought me a toy submarine, that I had admired at Simon Artz, the Harrods of Egypt. It smelled of incense. Although fully operational in the cabin bath, it would not surface as successfully as it dived. Perhaps this was why I did not volunteer to specialise in submarines.

Passage through the Suez Canal should have been simple and certainly "money for old rope" as far as the Company pilot was concerned. The south-bound convoy, in which we were the only warship, should have passed the north-bound column in the Great Bitter Lakes. But both movements were now out of phase, due, it was said later, to an enemy mine lay.

Our convoy was ordered to "gare up" to the canal bank to allow the others to pass. This manoeuvre, comfortable for a slab-sided merchant

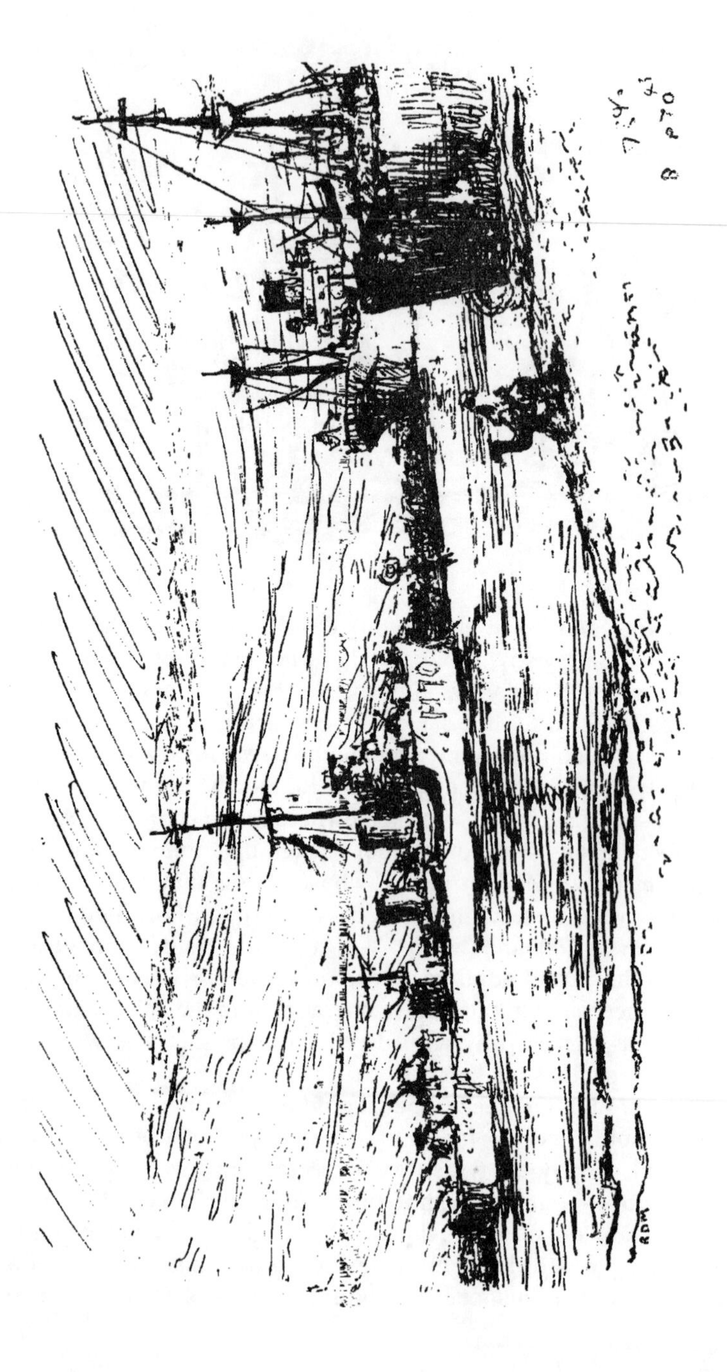

vessel, was bad news for a destroyer with its unprotected propellers, thin plating and engine room inlets and suctions. Several members of the ship's company immediately volunteered for the Camel Corps. There were noisy lamentations on the bridge, when, after hauling away from a passing caravanserai, we staggered to a halt and a single anchor with condenser inlets occupied by desert sand and a shoal of fish. Not for the first or last time I raised my hat to the Black Gang, our Engine Room Department, who got us under way. Months later, the ship was surprised to receive a letter of apology from an unusually polite Suez Canal company.

On we went fast through the Red Sea, with a stop for fuel at Aden, where some of us enjoyed a swim at Goldmohur, a rectangle of sea surrounded by steel nets to keep out shark and barracuda. Meanwhile, a diver inspected the ship's inlets. A dispute emerged over the Admiralty's recommendation to precede such an event with a couple of hand grenades to discourage hungry predators. The opposite view, which eventually prevailed, maintained that the explosions would only act as a sub-surface dinner gong.

My twenty-first birthday on 25th February coincided with an operationally uneventful passage of the Arabian Sea. The ship was unhappy. Embarrassingly explicit graffiti, such as *Altmark* (i.e. *Graf Spee*'s overcrowded prison ship), and "Hell Ship" appeared in red paint on the upper deck superstructure, and were removed as soon as seen by the management. Conditions in the mess decks, with scuttles closed by deadlights to darken ship and as a damage control precaution, were humid and excessively hot. It was quite clearly not an occasion for celebration and so I was only too happy for this historic event to pass unnoticed.

At about this time the *Exeter*, two Dutch cruisers and several destroyers were being demolished by a more powerful Japanese force in the Java Sea. Meanwhile, we sat in Bombay at the bottom of the hottest drydock in Asia, dominated by persistent flies, to rectify minor damage to a propeller suffered in the Canal event. When I was very small my father used to tell me to tuck my shirt in. "You look like a Bombay silk merchant." Silk merchants were not much in evidence, but stunningly beautiful Eurasian tarts, more like courtesans, paraded close by in horse-drawn gharries, sporting elegantly coloured parasols in the burning sun. These expensive ladies were, as far as Jolly Jack was concerned, just a mirage in a misbegotten, smelly and beerless desert. Stripey, evidently deprived, remarked that he felt randy enough "to stuff a ringbolt". Stripey's runs ashore, though infrequent, tended to be spectacular. On this occasion he fulfilled the role of Greek Chorus.

On we sped chasing flying fish and dolphins to Colombo for fuel. No sign of war, or preparation for it, was to be seen – only a momentary and tantalising glimpse of prewar colonial life-style and idle (as we were

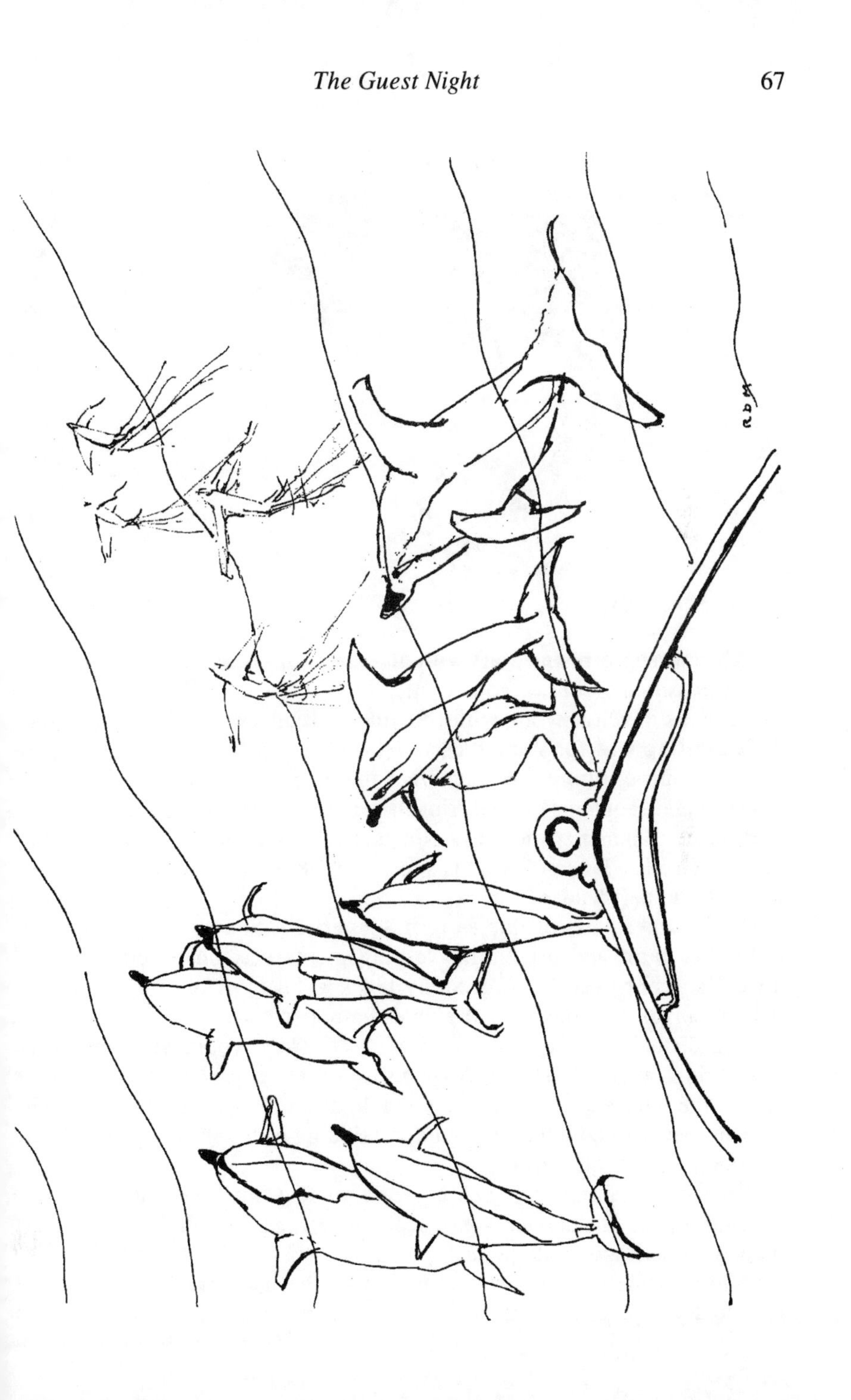

convinced) shore-bound staff with glamorous bronzed goddesses dressed in white, called Wrens, in tow. Cynically we skirted south of Ceylon (now Sri Lanka) to rendezvous with the elderly light aircraft carrier *Hermes*. This meeting was for some reason delayed, which was fortunate in view of that ship's future. We entered the beautiful natural harbour of Trincomalee, aquamarine and fringed with silver sand and graceful palms, berthing at Shamanzi fuel jetty alongside a sister ship, *Foxhound*, Commander Gordon Peters. With his superior rank he was, we assumed, to be our flotilla "half leader".

Unlike other parts of this eastern Shangri-La, Shamanzi with its large ugly tank farm and oil fuelling arrangements was unattractive. It was airless and unbelievably hot. Shiny black gobbets of oil floated around. White canvas awnings spread above the upper deck to fend off the sun were a distant memory from prewar days. They would have interfered with firing the guns. The stink of furnace fuel oil permeated. The shore end of the jetty was engulfed by a tangle of uninviting secondary jungle. Mosquitoes whined lethally around, reminding us to take the prophylactic pills that turned one yellow.

We secured alongside, looking forward to some well-earned, as we thought, sleep. The captain announced, in the same breath that he rang off main engines and without any preamble, "Guest Night tonight". The captain's pronouncement, which might have been a clever idea if handled differently, was made without any preliminary discussion with the First

Lieutenant who, as the wardroom mess president, should have been consulted. Such an event in the Navy is a formal dinner in the wardroom with, when possible, better than usual cuisine and wine, to which friends can be invited. It culminates in port being passed and a number of toasts, both traditional and those appropriate to the day of the week and the occasion, winding up with informal jollity and sometimes unsuitably athletic party games. The appropriate toast on this occasion would have been "A bloody battle or a foul pestilence". These two activities owed their celebration to the consequent promotion of survivors.

Everyone was astonished. At first it was thought to be a bad joke. Except for *Foxhound*'s officers, who like ourselves we suspected – rightly as it turned out – only wanted to sleep, there was no potential guest for

miles around, except perhaps a socially inclined parrot or monkey. Besides, the larder was now reduced to dried vegetables and the type of tinned meat known as "Corned Dog". Meanwhile, what Intelligence there was indicated that a powerful and modern Japanese fleet complete with up-to-date aircraft carriers was advancing in our direction across the Bay of Bengal in an unfriendly manner. Stories about the fatalistic brutality and cruelty to prisoners of our new enemy had filtered through. Not that it was something anyone thought about.

"Number One" went to see the captain privately. He explained that the officers wanted, and really needed, a quiet night. He argued that the idea of such an *ad hoc*, arbitrary and artificial entertainment would be very much resented under the present difficult conditions, with the ship expecting to be in action shortly against a formidable and indeed probably overwhelming enemy. He suggested that the Reserve officers might react adversely. After all, they had joined to fight the war and not to run a peacetime Navy. He thought of, but did not mention Drake, playing bowls before engaging the Spanish Armada. It did not help his case. Besides, this historical precedent might even have been in the captain's mind.

None of this had any effect. He was peremptorily ordered to get on with it and arrange a Guest Night, and that all officers were to attend and to wear Number 10 rig. Only some of us would have had white mess jackets on board. Number 10 rig consisted of a white starched cotton drill suit with brass buttons, shoulder straps and a high collar. In a closed-down compartment in the Tropics with no air conditioning, it is not what one would choose to wear. All officers were specifically told that this was a direct order from the captain and that everyone must attend without fail. An order given in such a manner in the Navy cannot by the regulations be ignored without serious disciplinary repercussions.

I think the doctor may have cleverly excused himself with a self-inflicted medical certificate. Otherwise at eight o'clock precisely all officers were present in the wardroom and the occasion looked as if it might after all be reasonably cheerful. The mess silver and trophies had been landed at the outbreak of hostilities, but what little remained had been rubbed up and now decorated the polished table. Cleared away at Action Stations the same table would have been otherwise prepared for the surgeon's activities. Place cards were prominent, even though everyone knew who everyone else was and precisely where to sit. Aloft, Sooty, judging by smell, clatter and smoke signals, and anxious about the Captain's emphasis on quality rather than quantity, was evidently concocting something delicious from brown Windsor, tinned herring in tomato sauce and Shepherd's Balls. Pink gin and sherry (Chez Saccone and Speed) were sampled for travel worthiness. A passable claret and a much voyaged port were lined up for the table. The junior steward refereed a dispute between two cockroaches over a crumb on the sideboard. The war was not mentioned.

The captain appeared suddenly in the doorway. His officers stood up. They were all in sparkling white uniform. But while the three R.N. officers were in formal Number 10s as ordered, the Reserves, R.N.R. and R.N.V.R., were wearing tropical rig, that is an open-neck shirt with shoulder straps, shorts and white shoes and stockings. Sensible and cool as it was, it was not what they had been directly ordered to wear by the captain.

The First Lieutenant welcomed our master with more than usual formality. There was a moment of suspense, while he glared at us and we looked

blank. I felt a chill down my back. Suddenly the face in the doorway convulsed and darkened. Halfway between a scream and a croak, there came a noise rather like that of a great injured bird. His arms flapped. "You are under arrest," he shouted and then vanished.

Winging his way over the brow to *Foxhound* past a surprised quartermaster, he sought advice (we guessed) from her captain. This was a sensible thing to do. It was just as well that the two ships were in company, but what Commander Gordon Peters actually said we would never know.

Dénouement: Captain and three depressed R.N. officers, the First Lieutenant, Gunner (T) and myself, ate a socially difficult and physically disgusting dinner in the captain's tin box of a harbour cabin. We sweated in silence until visibly pink through soaked white uniforms. Meanwhile, three of us disloyally envied the convivial hubbub, penetrating the bulkhead, generated by the Reserves, as they enjoyed their own Guest Night in the Wardroom. Familiar ditties such as "Lloyd George Knew My Father", "The Cow kicked Nelly in the Belly in the Barn" and "The Eton Boating Song" were only too recognisable. We all knew that this relaxed hilarity would have been inconceivable if the Captain had been in the Wardroom. What the stewards thought, or retailed forward to Jack, we did not care to think.

This protest, however ludicrous, was by definition a mutiny. Nothing more was ever heard of it. Nevertheless, the captain had now become, in the eyes of his officers, a lame duck.

Chapter 9

Canteen Boat

Strange consorts rode beside us
And brought us evil luck;
The witch fire climbed our channels,
And flared on vane and truck.
Rudyard Kipling

Winston Churchill summed up this period: "Breath-taking events were now to take place in the Bay of Bengal and the Indian Ocean. On March 28 Admiral Somerville received information of an impending attack on Ceylon by powerful Japanese forces including aircraft carriers about April 1."[1]

Java had now fallen, another devastating debacle. The consequent loss of my own father's livelihood – rubber, tea and coffee – I did not even think of. It had paled into insignificance. Burma was invaded and allied

shipping slaughtered in the Bay of Bengal. India was threatened, as was our supply line round the Cape to the Middle East. Churchill's speeches maintained faith in the face of what he himself described as a cataract of disasters. The news could not be worse. News was itself actually rationed, like petrol and sugar, which was perhaps as well, because it was all bad. What there was came in a short and, we suspected, deliberately dull and frequently corrupt daily signal from the Admiralty. Newspapers were months old and personal radio receivers of appropriate capability not in those days available to us.

The junior ship in a flotilla got all the odd jobs and was, and still is, known as the Canteen Boat. During the months of March and April 1942 *Fortune* flogged miles and miles of ocean. History is unlikely to record, or detect, what effect this little ship's activity had on the war effort, but the hithering and thithering did demonstrate a serious shortage of escorts for the conduct of a World War. As far as the Eastern Fleet was concerned, the pattern of operations was totally dictated by the Imperial Japanese Navy, now at the height of spectacular success.

We were ordered to sail back to Aden with *Foxhound*, who, perhaps to test or, even more likely, to tease our captain, placed him in tactical control for the passage. Owing to his customary delegation this ploy merely tested the sublieutenant. It was a fast run to rendezvous with the aircraft carrier *Indomitable*, Captain Denis Boyd. Arriving off Aden, referred to by Jack as "the arse hole of the Empire", in nil visibility and a sand storm, I was lucky enough to make a satisfactory landfall on the "Barren Rocks" down a fortuitous shore wireless bearing.[2] As one of Mark Twain's characters remarked, "It was wonderful that Columbus discovered America: it would have been more wonderful still if he had missed it." The truth is that I was still delighted and rather surprised when my homework turned out to be right.

After an abortive dummy torpedo attack on the carrier, for which neither ship gained marks from her captain, a well-known expert in the subject, the two destroyers screened *Indomitable* from Aden to Addu Atoll to join the Eastern Fleet. There was no moon and night was as black as boot polish. She stationed the two destroyers on a close anti-submarine screen almost under her bows. A broad zigzag was ordered. This was timed as usual by a clock on each bridge. It was so dark that it was difficult to see when the carrier had started her turn. Also, because of her rectangular silhouette, and with no navigation lights, it was often not easy to detect if she had turned the wrong way. It was dangerous to rely totally on the clock or the zig-zag diagram.

It took a quarter of an hour to turn over a bridge watch and to make sure that your relief had acquired his night vision. At the end of one middle watch (midnight to 4.00 a.m.), the competent Fred had taken over from me. I went aft to check that the upper deck was properly secured. Suddenly I became aware of an immense dark shape looming overhead. We were nearly done for. It was *Indomitable*'s bows. She had zigged the wrong way and slid past a sliver astern.

The following night *Fortune* was transfixed by a dramatic and eerie display of St. Elmo's fire, luminescently green, glowing at the end of every yardarm. That Kipling's "witch fire" was known to be a discharge of static electricity did not discourage the ship's company from sardonic comments about what such a portent might indicate.

At last Addu Atoll rose from the horizon; first a line of emerald palms and feathery Casuarina trees from which, alongside the entrance to the lagoon, sprouted the Port War Signal Station, a Nelsonic erection complete with awning, masts, flags, semaphore arms and flashing signal lamps. Brilliantly white coral divided the island from the sea, in which each green reflected and competed with another. Football-jersied fish abounded. It was beautiful, but not to be enjoyed by us. Fuelling in a hurry from a lonely rusting oiler, we left immediately to join the fleet.

On 24th March we rendezvoused with the 3rd Battle Squadron seeing a foursome of historic silhouettes from a remote position on the wedge-shaped screen. "Flat irons" they were facetiously called, and certainly the 15-inch gun battleships, *Resolution*, *Ramilles*, *Royal Sovereign* ("Tiddly Quid" to Jack) and *Revenge*, were impressive monuments to times past, when no threat from the air existed except from seagulls. Peacetime economy, Appeasement and Pacifism (short title PAP) had combined to ensure that not one of these dinosaurs had been modernised or replaced. Museum pieces, they were desperately slow and every one a potential coffin, when matched against up-to-date ships and up-to-date aircraft.

Meanwhile the so-called First Eleven, consisting of the aircraft carriers, *Indomitable*, *Formidable* and *Hermes* (the embarked air group known to be inexperienced) with the partially modernised battleship *Warspite*, were deployed somewhere between Addu and Ceylon. We were seeking, or more correctly waiting for, an action which was unlikely to be recorded as a great victory, that is at least by the Royal Navy. It was not for us to reason why, nor did we because there was no alternative.

The Eastern Fleet liked its commander. Genial and successful Admiral Sir James Somerville, now flying his flag in *Warspite*, had preceded *Fortune* from Force H. Not that we ever saw him in the flesh, the two squadrons being sensibly dispersed. His second in command, with his flag in *Resolution*, leading the Third Battle Squadron – our lot – was the not so popular, astringent, but undoubtedly effective, Vice Admiral "Algy" Willis,[3] who had frightened us midshipmen when he was chief of staff to Admiral Cunningham in the Mediterranean Fleet. Like Cunningham, Willis was monosyllabic, belonging to the "Never complain, never explain" school. One drawback of this enigmatic style lay in subordinates being faced with trying to surmise the reason for a policy or a plan, which

Willis.

in the circumstances, and with the limited information available, might seem unreasonable to the uninitiated.

On the anti-submarine screen, composed of twelve to fifteen destroyers, life was frustrating. Changes of course, position, night intentions and so on were, to preserve wireless silence, signalled by flag or light (very high frequency radio voice we did not have). At night the light was blue and only just visible. Being a very junior ship, and so far away, an order was usually executed by the flagship before we had received it along the line. This meant guesswork on the hoof. Similarly signalled night intentions rarely reached us in a complete state. It would have upset a cool and experienced destroyer captain. The effect on our excitable master was akin to spontaneous combustion. I had a horror of finding *Fortune* at dawn utterly alone on the ocean.

"Pilot," (I had progressed from Sub), "what's happened to the main body? I can't see it anywhere?"

"Sorry, sir, must have missed a signal during the night."

Fortune was regularly unpopular with the screen commander for being inside proper station, her officers-of-the-watch believing it best to "hold tightly on to nurse for fear of finding something worse".

The Royal Navy, mistakenly relying on historic coaling stations, had between the two World Wars neglected to adopt the technique of underway replenishment. The U.S. Navy did not make the same mistake. Because of this serious deficiency the fleet, and particularly its short-legged destroyers, were forced to return frequently to Addu Atoll to oil, usually in pitch darkness and sometimes a gale. *Fortune* was nearly always last in and first out of the lagoon, the privilege of being "Canteen Boat".

Our cheerful little Head "Poker", Chief Stoker Petty Officer Morris, prudently filled the oil fuel tanks to the brim and sometimes beyond. The crown of one tank, situated immediately below my cabin, arched due to the pressure. My only rug now slithered about on a film of the sticky, smelly, black stuff, which had forced its way upwards between riveted overlaps of steel plating.

Yesterday's battleships with leaky valves, joints and inefficient evaporators ran short of the fresh water essential for boilers and hydraulics. Their people were tightly rationed for washing, cooking and drinking to half a gallon a day. The destroyers were better off for water, but ran out of potatoes. Sailors loathe yams, the oriental alternative. Cockroaches in squadrons embarked with the victuals, accompanied by the occasional rat taking up whiskery residence in ventilation trunking.

There was a sinister resemblance to the material state and living conditions of Rozhestvensky's Imperial Russian Fleet, that in 1905 ploughed its way east across the same Ocean to be annihilated by the Japanese Navy in the straits of Tsushima. There was one significant difference. This lay in the quality of the Eastern Fleet's officers and men in morale, discipline and training (*Fortune*'s difficulties were abnormal), together with an undiminished belief in eventual victory, whatever might happen in battle. In the Tsar's fleet the officers were incompetent. But although many a good tune can be played on an old fiddle, the disgraceful obsolescence of our ships, due to political scrimping and professional failure to keep pace with modern sea warfare, put at desperate risk the lives of those who manned them.

A heaving line from a big ship under way provided yeast, (loud cheers), when our own bug died. Bread returned to the menu. Mail was sporadic and took a long time to get there. Conditions in the mess decks were hot, humid, crowded and generally deplorable with deadlights closed. "Cooks of the mess", self taught in culinary matters, chopped raw meat up on the mess table in among the slung hammocks of watchkeepers off watch and asleep, then took the result, labelled for ownership, to the galley for the

ship's company qualified "chef" to usher it in a professional manner through the oven door. The only pin-ups were of Jane, the *Daily Mirror* cartoon.

Skin infections, painted by the doctor in red or purple to taste, were evident for all to see as we wore nothing but shorts and sandals, and were otherwise brown as berries and hatless, a change from the Solar "topi" helmets of my childhood and a contrast to medical advice fifty years later. *Fortune*'s officers unanimously contracted conjunctivitis, not a pretty sight. Unpleasant as life was for Jack, there would have been no volunteers to transfer to Arctic convoys or the Army in North Africa.

On 2nd April, some eighty miles south of Ceylon, *Fortune* was jolted by a dim flashing light from the Battle Squadron flagship, *Resolution*. "Proceed and search for survivors of S.S. *Glenshields* torpedoed in 25 00 South 78 30 East."

"Course, Course," shouted the captain, rushing from one side of the bridge to the other in his haste to show that we knew where we were and the exact direction to go without the slightest delay. Three figures emerged miraculously from the top of my head and off we went at full speed. It was a relief to be independent again, clear of well-earned badgering for our many inefficiences.

Some 450 miles further on, having allowed a bit for drift with the help of a wind and ocean current map, extracted from the *National Geographic*

magazine, I announced with diffidence, understandable in the circumstance, that we were in position, and would now have to set off on an expanding search to look for the *Glenshield*'s lifeboats. As if on cue, the masthead lookout in the crows nest, Ordinary Seaman Trehearne, the youngest sailor in the ship, who had just pulled up a billy can of tea on a line, called out, "Sail bearing Green two zero", followed shortly by "four boats on the starboard bow". Such a timely interception made me rather pleased with myself, although the credit must go to the efficient organisation within the S.S. *Glenshields*, where following standard routine the Officer of the Watch passed an accurate position every half hour to the radio operator for distress purposes.

The survivors included women and children. These were accommodated somehow, one young couple and baby in my cabin. They were amazed how very small and uncomfortable a naval officer's cabin was and even more by the oily deck. I was rather put out, being proud of my palace, about the same size as a third class railway sleeper and a bunk rather more comfortable than the hammock in a passage that I had occupied in *Valiant*. With, on the bulkhead, three coloured prints, Cézanne's poplars, Cotman's "Greta Bridge" and Manet's "Bar at the Folies-Bergere", it should have been some improvement on any open ship's lifeboat. Their legacy, poor things, having lost everything except what they had been wearing at the time, was a lingering smell of unwashed humanity.

There had been no casualties. The U-boat, German and not Japanese, had been unexpectedly conscientious (and trusting) in giving a preliminary warning, so that the ship could first be abandoned. Stories of Hitler's increasingly nasty activities – death camps – had begun to trickle through and the standard U-boat attack was made without warning. *Glenshield*'s survivors were speedily embarked in case *Fortune*, lying stopped, became the next victim. The lifeboats were sunk by gunfire. The ship had been bound for Australia unescorted with a cargo of cotton "piece-goods". At the time we thought this a curious example of mis-applied war effort when ships were as precious as gold dust. The master appeared to have no idea of what his next cargo on return might be, and it could well have been essential grain or meat from Australia. Certainly slow merchantmen without an escort were only fodder for U-boats, as the United States Navy had already found out to its cost that year off the East coast of America. The records show that Allied shipping losses in March 1942 had been 834,000 tons (274 ships).

To amuse the children, the ship's company, led by ebullient Mess Deck Petty Officer Squires, generously assisted by his arch-rival, the Chief

Boatswain's Mate, known as Sunny Jim owing to a generous display of gold fillings, organised a traditional Crossing the Line ceremony. Held on the forecastle with King Neptune, barber, bears and all the trimmings, the dunking and shaving were made unusually precise by an anti-submarine zigzag steered along the equator to Addu Atoll. There our passengers were transferred to a Royal Fleet Auxiliary, to their relief as well as ours. But this was not before they had been publicly harangued by the captain on no account to talk to anyone about this "Top Secret anchorage". Although he was right, it was also the only occasion that he ever attempted a public address. *Glenshield*'s Chief Officer knew the place only too well, having been wrecked there in a three-masted sailing ship many years before.

Chapter 10

Beating Retreat

Jam yesterday, jam tomorrow, but never jam today.

We now know that at this time General Nagumo with four of the fast carriers that had been employed on the attack on Pearl Harbour, and four battleships, were off the South of Ceylon, his aim being to exterminate the Eastern Fleet.

On 5th April *Fortune* was urgently despatched to search for a suspected German raider, disguised as a merchant ship, said to be 250 miles to the North. There were several of these operating in the Indian Ocean and Pacific.[1]

On the same day intercepted signals were received from the 8-inch gun cruisers *Dorsetshire* and *Cornwall* reporting that they were under air attack in a position between us and Ceylon. I plotted this on the primitive automatic local operations table in the wheelhouse. This hub of information, usually decorated with cocoa cups and his cigar, was effectively manned by urbane Leading Supply Assistant (Hostilities Only) Galloway, without any training for such a duty before joining *Fortune*.

Silence followed the first reports. The tragic loss of both ships, not too far away, yet more out-of-date sitting ducks with no air defence, had to be assumed. It was typical of James Somerville that he insisted against the advice of his staff and the Flag Office Second in Command on taking the fleet to rescue the Survivors of *Dorsetshire* and *Cornwall*. But we only knew of this later. There was, owing to rigid wireless silence, no indication on our plot where the rest of the fleet was at this time. Nor was there any up-to-date information on the enemy, except for the powerful listed Order of Battle, very much a sophisticated First Eleven in ships and aircraft, provided by Intelligence. We felt distinctly lonely. In retrospect

Fortune was far less vulnerable when on her own than with the fleet, a dedicated target of the Imperial Japanese Navy. The next bad news was that Colombo, Capital of Ceylon, had been attacked by a large carrier-borne bomber force, but with what result we were not told.[2]

Meanwhile, I nearly succeeded in doing the enemy's job for him by advising the captain in an excess of confidence that it was safe to pilot the ship through Kolumadulo, a huge Atoll, some 250 miles north of Addu, to investigate what appeared in the distance to be a suspicious vessel at anchor, which might just be our quarry. It would have taken twice as long to circle the atoll, perhaps allowing it to escape. Once committed to the risky adventure I discovered too late that the chart, although recently surveyed, bore little resemblance to the reality of growing coral heads. There was no turning back. Perched precariously on top of the front of the bridge, I conned the ship using the colour of the sea, guided by the mast head lookout in the crow's nest. The different colours indicated in the sunlight the approximate depth of the often dangerously shallow water (a dodgy, but useful, technique gleaned from the Indian Ocean Sailing Directions). Depth was confirmed anxiously, and too late anyway, by both echo sounder and a leadsman on the forecastle, who judging by his voice was as frightened as I was when he got to calling "Deep Four (twenty-four feet)".

The suspected enemy raider turned out to be a vintage and conspicuous, but uncharted wreck. We had too nearly joined it. I was thankful that luck had yet again been with *Fortune*, but it was a breathtaking experience. Returning to Addu to fuel, we sailed once again to rejoin the 3rd Battle Squadron on 9th April. On the same day the light aircraft carrier, *Hermes*, whom *Fortune* had earlier been earmarked to join, was sunk with both her escorts by Japanese air attack southeast of Trincomalee, which was also bombed.

It became clear, although nothing was said, that the Eastern Fleet, which had been seeking the enemy in the best "Rule Britannia", "Engage the enemy more closely" tradition, and with many otherwise stout hearts hoping that the unmatched twain would never meet, was now to be withdrawn to remain strategically "in being" in safer waters. We were indeed beating retreat. It had been recognised that the Eastern Fleet was no match for an up-to-date Japanese Task Force with its powerful Carrier Air Group. The historian Mahan's "fleet-in-being" did not refer to a bunch of hulks.

No one at the time realised that the powerful enemy was doing exactly the same, albeit for different reasons but not before it had created mayhem in the Bay of Bengal, sinking as many of our unprotected merchantmen as were lost in the awful PQ17 Russian envoy only thirteen weeks later.[3] It was only much later it became clear that the Japanese War Machine, carried away by unexpected success, was now seriously over-extended. Their army had not the capability (they estimated five divisions) to occupy Ceylon.[4] The attack on Pearl Harbour had failed to find and destroy the U.S. Carrier Force. But we knew none of this at the time, and probably had we known would have taken it with a pinch of salt.

The 3rd Battle squadron lumbered majestically westwards across the Indian Ocean to Mombasa, dolphins with their built-in higher speed at play around bluff bows, and tails very much between legs. It was the custom before the days of electronic navigation for all ships to hoist a flag signal, when ordered to do so, each giving her own estimate of the noon position. This public performance naturally interested commanding officers, ours no less than others. He would become agitated in case there was a significant discrepancy between my calculation and that of the flagship. About twenty-four hours before we reached our destination, up went the strings of coloured flags and it was obvious that my estimate, which I knew to be good, having collected several stars and a sun sight, was about sixty miles (that is one whole degree of latitude) to the north of the flagship's.

"Haul it down!" bawled the captain, jumping up and down with anxiety. "Adjust the hoist!"

Yeoman Cromwell, knowing the game, as did his opposite numbers in other ships, had cunningly arranged the flag hoist on the blind side of the mast. Not for nothing were signalmen known as bunting tossers. No more was said. The following morning the coast of Africa turned up to agree with me (and presumably all the other unqualified destroyer navigators) and not with the flagship. The C.O. was happy about this, because there had been no argument with higher authority, exacerbated by the ultimate sin of being proved right.

Shortly after our arrival at Kilindini, Mombasa, a troop ship entered harbour crammed with soldiers who had escaped from Singapore. As it passed each warship in the crowded anchorage in turn the ships' companies of their own accord booed heartily and whistled. There were cries of "Got your running shoes?" It was disgraceful, but such things happen in war.[5] Ironically, Jack seemed completely unaware that he had just completed a similar, if overtly more dignified, manoeuvre.

A day or two were spent in long overdue boiler cleaning,[6] weapon maintenance and storing. I helped with a hydrographic survey of the

anchorage. Jack investigated the doubtful facilities of Mombasa. One afternoon the Wardroom took the motor boat away on a banyan (picnic) party, well supplied with iced lime juice laced with gin. Philip Archer-Shee provided three attractive young FANYs (First Aid Nursing Yeomanry) for company. Normally seen dressed overall in khaki skirts and polished brown mosquito boots, on this occasion the ladies emerged to our delight in what would in due course of time be called Bikinis. Very susceptible to feminine charms, whether or not I was inspired or overwhelmed by this display I cannot remember. But I was as fit as a fiddle. Bursting with energy I ran on my own for about three miles or so across virgin beaches of sand and mud, under and around twisting mangrove trees, the sweat pouring off my back. By this time we were all impervious, or so we thought, to the tropical sun and everything else.

The following day the ship was ordered to shift from our berth alongside a battleship, to an anchor berth. I felt strangely light-headed, as I climbed the bridge ladder, and collapsed beside the compass when taking a bearing. Shortly afterwards I was carted ashore unconscious to Mombasa military hospital. My face was blue and my condition, in the opinion of knowledgeable members of the ship's company, terminal.

Chapter 11

Vigorous Up

Oh, the grand old Duke of York;
He had ten thousand men.

He whom the gods favour dies young.
Plautus

Was it a nightmare? I came to on a stretcher under a thatched roof supported by tree trunks and open to the air in every direction. A wind blew. Alongside me two human spars vanished upwards into an equally

stupendous arrangement of khaki. Somewhere up above I could make out a scarlet female, but not very maternal, face under a cap ornamented with the brass insignia of Aesculapius. Ants scurried about. I felt like one.

It was as cold as charity is supposed to be, and I said so vigorously before passing out. It was not funny to be deliberately left out in the cold. In reality the air temperature was tropical. Some days later a pretty nurse told me that my sea-faring language on this occasion, of which I had no recollection, had entertained bystanders, but not the senior medical lady. My repertoire would have benefited from hearing Number One fending off bum boats in Port Said, "Your mother is in bed with the postman." "Your grandfather's pox has obviously been transmitted."

Apparently torpedoed by pneumonia, I would have sunk without trace had it not been for a newly invented drug, Sulphonamide, the original antibiotic. This was a product of Meyer and Baker. Now I was really in debt to one enemy.

Patients in the ward included an army officer in the terminal stage of blackwater fever, and a naval gunnery specialist whiling away sickness by writing a novel in the style of Charles Morgan. Opposite was a cheerful young paymaster lieutenant, life and soul of the party. We teased him unmercifully when it was decided that, while he was there for some other ailment, it would be as well to remove his tonsils. Later a subdued nurse made his bed up. The poor man had died under the anaesthetic. The next morning our good physician was himself horizontal with malaria.

On the day of my discharge I discovered, by nearly sinking, that I was not in condition to complete even a single length of the Mombasa Club swimming pool. Awarded ten days sick leave, on arrival at Nairobi and given the choice of Town or Country hospitality, I opted for rural life and was entertained by the owners of a comfortable country hotel.[1] I saw miles and miles of exciting and beautiful landscape. Wildlife was everywhere, including in the Muthaiga Club the notorious scandal-driven Delves-Broughton cum Erroll menage,[2] elegantly grotesque in garden party hats with a conspicuous lack of attention to wartime utility clothing. In Nairobi it was difficult to believe that elsewhere people were fighting for their lives and, so we believed, for the future of democracy and civilisation.

I rejoined *Fortune* at Mombasa. None of us knew at the time that the U.S. Pacific Fleet had just dramatically fended off a Japanese Carrier Force, including the Task Force so recently threatening the Eastern Fleet, in the Battle of The Coral Sea. This was a major and significant victory, a turning point in the Far East War. While I had been ashore *Fortune* had taken part in Operation *Ironclad*, the capture of Diego Suarez on 7th May from the Vichy French. This vast bay in Madagascar was capable of accommodating the British fleet or the Japanese, whichever got there first.

The ship's participation on the covering force screen had been uneventful, unlike that of the destroyer *Anthony*, Lt. Commander J.M. Hodges. She penetrated the Diego harbour defences at night, made a sternboard alongside and landed fifty Royal Marines, hastily collected from big ships' detachments, including Wardroom Mess Attendants, in the surprised rear of the French Army. The otherwise well-dug-in garrison then capitulated. During my absence I gathered that Number One had taken a

personal interest in *Fortune*'s safe navigation, a skill in which he was after all a master.

Fortune was then ordered to rejoin the Mediterranean Fleet at Alexandria for an undisclosed operation. We sped helter-skelter back round Cape Gardafui, the Horn of Africa, off which fork-tailed frigate birds incessantly and ominously, because it recalled the Lufftwaffe, dive on boobies, an occupation which appears fifty years later to have infected the local inhabitants.[3] Then on we went through the Red Sea and Suez Canal, emerging from Port Said into the Mediterranean on 11th June.

The following day at a buoy in Alexandria harbour was occupied in absorbing the orders for Operation *Vigorous*. The aim was to fight through to beleaguered Malta a supply convoy of modern fast merchant vessels. A smaller convoy was timed to leave Gibraltar for the same destination (Operation *Harpoon*). How this fitted into the jigsaw of the Mediterranean War, as seen by either side, is clear from two quotations taken from Winston Churchill's *Memoirs*.[4]

> Erwin Rommel. April 1942.
> "The Panzer Army is to attack as soon as possible after the capture of Malta."
> Prime Minister to General Auchenleck. 10th May 1942.
> "The very latest date for engaging the enemy which we could approve is one which provides a distraction in time to help the passage of the June dark-period convoy."[4]

For the first, and only time, in the commission Flotilla (nowadays Squadron) specialist staff officers came on board to offer their assistance, and check up on our capability, for which I was grateful. The three lieutenants were: Brian Gallie,[5] signals; Julian Pearson, torpedoes; and Paul Whatley, navigation. They were a helpful, mature and amusing team, answering my questions with patience. It brought home how neglected *Fortune* had been elsewhere, as indeed she continued to be for the rest of the commission. This was due to inflexibility inherent in an administrative system not geared up for a World War, fought by so many widely dispersed and constantly on-the-move single ship units.

There was an explosion in the Wardroom doorway. My opposite number from *Decoy* had let off a Thunder Flash (firework supplied for training) on his arrival to take a drink off me. "A man is judged by his friends" was agreed by everyone now under the Wardroom table, but the diversion was what we needed. We had become too serious, particularly me.

By now the Mediterranean Fleet was much diminished from my days in the battleship *Valiant*, when a Malta convoy would have been covered by two aircraft carriers, five battleships and a mass of cruisers and destroyers. Now there were neither battleships, aircraft carriers nor air group, just eight cruisers and about twenty destroyers plus six borrowed from the Eastern Fleet,[6] with some rescue ships and minesweepers.[6] But there was still a formidable submarine flotilla based precariously at Malta.[7]

Libya was again in enemy hands, so continuous air attack could be expected and no shore-based fighter support from our own side worth mentioning. Acting Admiral Sir Henry Harwood (Battle of River Plate) was now C. in C., his flag in the battleship *Queen Elizabeth*, under repair in the floating dock after being damaged together with *Valiant* by Italian

manned torpedoes. It did not seem the same without Admiral Cunningham (ABC, Cuts or Meat Face, depending on how well you knew him), nor was it, as we were soon to find out.

Rear Admiral Philip Vian,[8] of *Cossack* and *Altmark* fame, commanded the escort force. He had a well-earned reputation as a ruthless and impolite martinet. I found his orders as clear and impressive as his war record, which included the defence of an earlier Malta convoy and second Battle of Sirte; although, such is the isolation of war, that we in *Fortune* knew

nothing of this action at the time. In him there was every reason to have confidence. It would have been nice if we had felt the same about our own master, brooding in silence like a morose raven on one side of the bridge. Subversively, I hoped that he would flap off his perch and croak away into the sunset.

While his officers took the brunt of his ill humour, they took care not to discuss him. Jack on the other hand, now far from Jolly, barely disguised his feelings. He was to some extent shielded by the cheerful and extrovert management of the First Lieutenant. Michael's personality was the jam that made the sandwich passable. He may have over-corrected with informality and a loose rein, but it worked. The rest of us did our best in dealing with people in our own Divisions (sections of sailors for whom we had personal responsibility). It did occur to me, and probably others, that our leader might disappear as the result of a push over the side one dark night. Such a scenario was really too unworthy to dwell on.

The senior rates looked confidently, and with good reason also, to the genial engineer officer, "Chiefy" Batt, who was much the oldest man in the ship; his balding pate, resembling a tonsure, reflected the midday sun. He enjoyed a rendering of Lewis Carroll's ditty,

> "Twinkle, Twinkle, little bat, how I wonder what you're at.
> Up above the world so high, like a tea tray in the sky."

The engineer's office became "The Belfry".

The officers' loyalty remained projected towards the captain as a matter of principle, an attitude which was the result of training rather than

regulation. Somehow, each of us found it helpful to close his mind to the nature of the oddball holding the appointment, hoping meanwhile that some weird command decision in battle would not result in *Fortune* "going gurgle gurgle".

Operation *Vigorous* kicked off serenely as planned from Alexandria on 13th June. The convoy of eleven merchant ships formed up.[9] Some appeared to be flying a white ensign rather than the customary red or blue. We heard that, because the convoy must get through willy nilly against a much superior opposition in this narrow sea fight, all crews had been required to sign T124X agreements, thus putting their officers and ratings under the Naval Discipline Act. At the time I wondered why this was necessary, knowing the Merchant Navy's sterling performance in the war. Later I heard that there had been some "infiltration of undesirables into the Merchant Navy Pool" as a consequence of manpower legislation in 1941, which was presumably an explanation. Merchant seamen were of course paid more than Jack.

The convoy were fast fine-looking cargo vessels and up to date. Not one was a "Smokey Joe" or potential straggler. With them were minesweepers and unarmed rescue ships. While the convoy formed up, the cruisers with flagship *Cleopatra* (Captain Guy Grantham, the politest and probably the nicest officer in the Navy[10]) took station near the main body. This consisted of a dummy and unconvincing "battleship", the ancient (vintage 1911) *Centurion*, manned by a small volunteer steaming crew. She had once upon a time been the radio-controlled target for fleet gunnery practice, but was now an unconvincing military fig leaf.

The destroyers formed a vast circular screen all the way round the convoy to maximise anti-aircraft protection. This lack of depth required by the priority of air defence, we realised would be good news for a U-boat. The main armament of prewar ships like *Fortune* had been designed to fight surface ships, not aircraft. Newer ships' armament was intended to be dual purpose. Our 20-mm Oerlikons and smaller machine guns, aimed only by eye, were effective against easy targets such as low fliers on a steady course at point blank range. For once *Fortune* on the southern perimeter was no more distant from the flagship than any other escort. This for some reason pleased the captain, but made others among us anxious.

Apart from a shadower buzzing round and reporting our position and composition, invulnerable because there was not a fighter to swat it, the remainder of the day was uneventful. We did not even qualify for our usual "Charlie Sugar" (take up your appointed station). Stripey blew up

his lifebelt remarking, "Here's the only fuckin' air support on tap today." That this observation was not original did not lessen its validity.

Night, for which the screen was adjusted to cope with attack by Fast Patrol Boats, short as it was in June, proved to be a prolongation of day, made so by a succession of brilliant parachute flares dropped one after the other overhead by enemy aircraft. There were some other alarums and excursions, but no material loss as far as we knew.

On the following day 14th the sky was Delft overhead fading to Wedgwood around the horizon. Puffs of cloud gambolled by like flocks of sheep. The sea was calm and every shade of blue and green, a poster for a Mediterranean cruise. The panorama of shipping stretched as far as the eye could see. Picked out in silver, violet and grey, it appeared motionless, although actually and purposefully heading westward for Malta. Then came an air raid warning and the first of one attack after another by bombers, German and Italian, from every quarter, from North Africa, Crete, Italy and Sicily. It was a mix of fifty or so aircraft at a time – high level, shallow dive and surface torpedo attacks. The destroyer screen was ordered to fire a pre-arranged Umbrella barrage. This ploy was an attempt to make up for a desperate lack of effective anti-aircraft weaponry.

Ships were required to fire their main armament, mostly 4.7-inch guns, repeatedly at maximum elevation (*Fortune*'s was only thirty-five degrees) in a metallic spray over the top of the convoy. Shells were fused by hand to go off at their zenith. Hit or miss, it was of course bound to be miss owing to the volume of empty space over one convoy when compared to the size of one aeroplane. But it presumably forced aircraft, at least the less intrepid, to fly high. Ineffective against high level fliers at 16,000 feet and expensive in ammunition, there was no alternative.

The noise was stupendous, a crescendo of bangs and thumps, interspersed with the crash of empty brass shell cases on the iron deck. The main enemy effort was aimed at the convoy, but from time to time great spouts rose round *Fortune*, presumably bombs dropped by design to make a hole in the defence, or by pilots distracted by the barrage, or just off-loading as an afterthought on the way home. One of several brave and suicidal attacks by Italian torpedo bombers on our side of the screen required these galumphing three-engined Savoias to pass between the destroyers close above the sea on a slow steady course. There was a loud cheer when Ordinary Seaman Fitzgerald (he who had accidentally fired the Snowflake rocket off Gibraltar) brought a Savoia down into the sea in flames with the starboard Oerlikon. Loud cheers from everybody. No time to think of the brave Italian airman.

The wind had freshened. Low clouds scudded overhead and obscured the sun.

Scene – The bridge. Action stations. I am Officer of the Watch.

JACK, a lookout. "Aircraft Red Four Oh Angle of sight Three Oh Close!"

O.O.W. (Officer of the Watch) to HELMSMAN. "Hard-a-port, Full ahead."

Ship heels violently to starboard as her bows swing to port. Immediate impulse as, throttles wide open, 36,000 shaft horsepower thrusts forward. Sea flattens in slick created within arc of ship's rapidly turning hull.

O.O.W. "Midships" . . . "Steady" (to point at attacker).

C.O., urgently "Open fire, Open fire!"

FIRST LIEUTENANT "Shoot."

FIREGONG, musically Ding Ding!

GUNS noisily Bang Crash Clatter Bonk Bang!

Acrid Cordite fumes, yellow and black, drift over front of bridge.

JACK, a lookout. "Diving now."

CO to HELMSMAN. "Hard-a-port," (to narrow target broadside on).
Twin-engined JU88 bomber with black cross markings thunders 500 feet overhead. Two finned bombs, inscriptions legible, whistle past. Unpleasant detonation in sea close on port quarter. Ship shakes like wet retriever.

Much black smoke from both funnels. Column of pea green sea water rises dramatically above masthead.

CHORUS "Phew!"

JACK, a lookout "Corfuck!"

FIRST LIEUTENANT "Well done, Jack!"

Fortune returned to her place on the screen and continued to offer a contribution to the barrage over the convoy. Splashes of one sort or another fell around. As they say, "what goes up must come down". A merchant ship was sunk, others damaged. A pall of smoke hung over the centre of the convoy within which a fire could be seen burning.

The telephone from the engine room howled urgently. The Engineer Officer, the Chief Engine Room Artificer and the Chief Stoker had been wounded, one of them seriously. A lull in action followed. It was established that an inadvertently unfused shell, fired from the other side of the destroyer screen, had struck the iron deck by the engineroom hatch and broken up into splinters. This spray of metal caught the Engineer and his two senior ratings standing together forward of the torpedo tubes watching the air attack, but poised just above their beloved and essential machinery in a spot, known as the "engineer's bridge".

"Chiefy" Batt died almost immediately. It was important to bury him before the next attack came in. The traditional arrangements were made. Sewn up in a hammock (last stitch traditionally through the nose – sailmaker's macabre precaution to detect any spark of life) – his body, weighted with shot and firebricks, was ready to be consigned to the deep. Fastened on top of the white ensign, which covered the lashed-up hammock and its seven round turns of rope, was Chiefy's battered blue uniform cap.

A funeral party from all departments was hastily mustered in the port waist abreast the forward funnel. The First Lieutenant went up to the bridge to ask the captain's approval to half-mast the ship's ensign, and then for him to come down to conduct the burial service on the iron deck.

There was a difficulty. The captain obstinately refused to half-mast the ensign without the Admiral's approval. This was something to do, it seemed, with his eccentric belief that such an action in battle might be interpreted as a signal of surrender. We tried to persuade him that our admiral and his staff had other things to think about than niceties of this sort, but he was adamant. The outcome of this embarrassing and absurd

argument, conducted in public on the bridge, was a compromise. The ensign, where it flew on the mainmast gaff, was momentarily dipped as the body went over the side. Later I heard that it was registered at the time in the flagship that something odd had gone on in *Fortune*, judging by an incomprehensible signal from her about ceremonial in battle.

It was overcast and miserable, and the west wind was lifting spray off steel grey wavetops when Lieutenant Commander Batt, R.N.R., was buried. The oldest man in the ship, he had been against all omens the gods' first choice; though they say that there are different ways of interpreting Plautus. We would miss his understated and sardonic personality, the irony and dotty stories, often relevant, about his peacetime role around the boilers and incinerators of a "loony bin".

Months later the First Lieutenant received a letter from "Chiefy's" widow asking about the circumstances of her husband's death. The standard Admiralty telegram had broken the tragic news, but not a word had come from his captain. This was a more than unfortunate omission. "*Dulce et decorum est pro patria mori*."[11]

Chapter 12

Vigorous Down

He marched them up to the top of the hill,
And he marched them down again.

The convoy was now south of Crete. The plot was confused. Attempting to penetrate and analyse the fog of war through the fog of tobacco in the wheel house was not easy. L.S.A. (Leading Supply Assistant) Galloway's cigar may have added tone but did not help. The paper and pencil surface,

on which a mechanical device driven by clockwork kept the dead reckoning position up to date, showed a paucity of information mainly gleaned from the officer of the watch; a few enemy reports received by wireless and, if the shore authority did its stuff, items re-broadcast from air reconnaissance. Of the last there was little so far. I could not help feeling that strict wireless silence on principle, when the other side knows all about you, does not make much sense.

Then an enemy report initiated, we heard later, by R.A.F. reconnaissance was received with the news that the Italian fleet had left its base in Taranto in force. Measurement showed that we should be in action by daylight. I went down to the chart house and opened Admiral Vian's orders for such an eventuality. It was one for which *Fortune* and her class of destroyer had actually been designed with torpedo tubes and high speed. We had even practised this manoeuvre with *Indomitable* as target off Aden – though the result had been a disaster.

The orders had the supreme virtue of clarity and simplicity. Destroyers on the side threatened by enemy heavy ships would form up for a torpedo attack in as near as possible a concave half circle, described as the shape of an open umbrella, with the handle aimed at the enemy and the ferrule pointed at our convoy. Umbrellas were evidently popular with the squadron staff. As torpedo control officer I was confident about how and when to fire them (torpedoes not umbrellas), if the opportunity arose, but I suspected that we would be shot to pieces if this manoeuvre took place in broad daylight, and this did appear likely if both forces continued on their present course and speed. Smoke screens laid by destroyers, pumping extra oil into their furnaces, would provide the only cover as at the Battle of Sirte.

My imagination took off. What if, under horrendous fire, *Fortune* succeeded even by mistake in clobbering a battleship with her torpedoes and the captain was awarded the D.S.C., perhaps even a D.S.O. for gallantry. Who knows? Frog turns into prince and all live happily ever after. More spectacular would be his posthumous V.C. I could see *Fortune*'s mast head and truck still just visible above the waves, while clinging to it our heroic Ahab, wrapped in an undulating white ensign, aimed his .22 rifle to demolish a final seagull before, clutching a copy of the King's Regulations and Admiralty Instructions and with his personally drafted citation, he sank to the satanic depths of Davy Jones' Locker. The only trouble with this scenario was that we would all be posthumous too.

There was an interlude in the bombing. I opened the chart house safe and took out two large Confidential Books, the Fighting Instructions and the Destroyer Fighting Instructions. If a surface action was in the offing it would be illuminating to see what the Naval Staff had to say on the subject. The former, a glossy, scarlet, expensively bound volume, appeared to be devoted to a re-run of the battle of Jutland. The blue, less ormolu, loose-leaf Destroyer publication also had absolutely no relevance to the impending engagement. Both books were heavily weighted with lead for sinking in extremis. Presumably this precaution was to avoid the contents astonishing an enemy in event of their capture.

Disillusioned, I returned gladly to the current operational orders. The suspense, waiting for battle, was rather like that I had experienced before entering the ring, when aged 14 and drawn to fight the champion in a school boxing competition. I comforted myself now, though far from proud of it at the time, because, egged on by my knowledgeable Second's encouraging, "He can slaughter you. You haven't a chance unless you clobber him quick", and with my eyes closed in sheer terror, I had floored the Champ with a totally unscientific and not exactly too fair haymaker. Boxing master was terribly upset.

The night was full of alarms, false and real. Sleep, a precious commodity in war and sampled in five minute snatches, proved to be, within realistic and cacophonous dreams, simply a continuation of the battle. I was up and down to the bridge from the charthouse. The big 6-inch gun cruiser *Newcastle* was torpedoed, probably by a fast patrol boat, her sister ship *Birmingham* damaged by a bomb and the destroyer *Hasty* sunk. Not that this information percolated immediately onto the wheelhouse plot. In the early hours of 15th the convoy course was reversed away from the enemy ships, but ordered back onto its westerly course towards Malta in the morning.

The reason for so many time-consuming reversals of our fifty-ship Armada was baffling – to those taking part. The Sultan of Turkey's Jannisery band, with two steps forward and one step back, made more progress. Historians believe that it was due to dithering by the new and inexperienced shore-based C. in C., who was involved in an operation which he had been ordered to carry out by the Admiralty probably against his better judgement.[1] Another reason, we guessed, was the lack of R.A.F. aircraft available for reconnaissance owing to the land battle in the Desert, and the very low priority allocated by the U.K. Air Staff to the Mediterranean.

An amplifying report arrived to say that two Italian 46,000 ton battleships *Vittorio Veneto* and *Littorio* were now 200 miles to the northwest with two heavy cruisers, two light cruisers and twelve destroyers in

company. The scenario, as I laid it out on the plotting table, began to resemble one of those paper battles "fought" between Blue and Red at action speed during technical courses by Sublieutenants under training. The assets in the current existence appeared to be unfairly loaded on the side of Red.

At 0940[2] when the Italian units were 150 miles, that is four or five hours, distant, our Armada was altered away for about two hours before again turning towards Malta. Meanwhile, air attacks continued. The convoy suffered terribly. Of the original eleven ships only six remained at this stage. The specialised rescue ships, we trusted, would pick up floating survivors. They, poor chaps, would soon be at sea in other ships, in other convoys, on other seas, many to die unknown and largely unappreciated.[3]

Early in the afternoon, as a direct result of this attrition, Vian was ordered by a signal from the C.-in-C. to turn the remaining ships of the convoy back to Alexandria. I have been told by a contemporary,[4] who was on the flagship's bridge, that this order, inevitable in the circumstances and some would say predictable, had quite evidently been a terrible one for Admiral Vian, with his admirable "press on to win" reputation, to receive. Even so, had we reached Malta there would not have been sufficient ammunition remaining in ships' magazines for the return trip to Alexandria.

Air attacks continued ferociously throughout the afternoon. It was absurdly easy to believe that one's own ship had become Luftwaffe target Number One. Thumping near misses activated adrenalin. A low level attack was countered in the same way as before. It had worked well also off Cape Bon in February.

In an attempt to keep men who were stationed between decks in the picture, I had arranged for my "tanky" (chart corrector), an intelligent, educated H.O. ordinary seaman, to broadcast a running commentary over the ship's system from the bridge. But I expected too much. Under fire his voice quavered. Though understandable, this defeated the object. A complaint from below reached me. I pulled the plug out when he was not looking. Unfortunately there was no one else to spare for this important task, so I did my best to fill in during lulls, rather like a third rate cricket commentator covering up for his own side's inadequate batting. Babbling into a microphone when under enemy fire, I realised, calls for a special sort of dedicated courage of the War Correspondent, quite distinct from that of the active warrior.

In war, Jack will willingly bargain away all his treasured comforts for extra ammunition to bang off at the enemy. This is in marked contrast to his attitude in peacetime. The First Lieutenant in the director control tower, a rotating steel mushroom above and abaft the bridge, was assessing the rapid expenditure of ammunition, not wanting to run out before reaching harbour. He also needed to have enough shots left in the locker to fight a surface action against heavy ships. Percentage of ammunition remaining was signalled regularly to the flagship whenever there was a lull.

The guns had stopped firing momentarily on his orders to conserve ammunition. The captain became like one possessed. His face black with rage, he leaned over the front of the bridge and screamed at A and B guns to open fire immediately, thereby short-circuiting his second in command. The terrible Petty Officer Jacko was the captain of B gun, which was nearest to the bridge. He led his crew well and his blood was up. A hefty man with a red face and towsled hair, he faced the bridge in front of his gun's crew, opened his overalls, and brandished his impressive family tree. If the captain saw this outrageous display or registered the abuse that accompanied it, as everyone else did, then he gave no sign.

Meanwhile, we became aware that the R.A.F. had managed to deploy a brave, if ineffective, effort at long range when a rubber dinghy floated by, out of which emerged two angry young aviators. These were the pilot and navigator of a Beaufighter, known to be under gunned and not fast enough. They complained bitterly that they had been shot down by their own flight commander during a confused dog fight. In the Navy we could not help being cynical about R.A.F. High Command with its "carpet bombing of Germany fixation" at the expense of their own Coastal Command and the Atlantic battle, which incidentally provided all its fuel. But this was neither the time nor place to discuss such a subject with our new

guests, particularly when R.A.F. Middle East was already over-stretched in support of the retreating Desert Army.

The bravery of bomber crews was not in question, although Jack did remark on the continuous publicity they received compared to rarely mentioned convoy duty. In the event an R.A.F. bomber succeeded in damaging *Littorio*, when she was on her way home (she had got within 100 miles of the convoy) and *Trento* with a torpedo. The latter was subsequently sunk by *Umbra*, Lt. Commander Lynch Mayden, from the Malta submarine flotilla.

Meanwhile another cruiser, *Hermione*,[5] had been torpedoed and the Australian destroyer *Nestor*[6] sunk. The night proved equally disturbing and sleepless, but no damage was registered. There were several reports enemy F.P.B.s (fast patrol boats) in the offing, which did little to clarify the chaos of battle.

Before reaching Alexandria there was an unusual event. This was a voluntary religious service of thanksgiving on the lee side of the torpedo tubes. It was well attended, the only time throughout the commission. Presumably, gratitude was being expressed by Jack for his own personal survival as well as his ship's.[7]

I do not think that any of us worried over much at being killed outright, except for regret at sudden and involuntary deprivation of the more attractive aspects of future life, love and maturity. Like Jack, it was not difficult to believe that one's own bullet had one's number on it. But most shared a horror of collecting an unpleasant and permanently crippling wound in an embarrassing place. Fortunately, when in action, there was no time to think about anything except the job in hand. One became curiously and illogically impervious without being in any way brave – a category, which it is said that *Fortune* favours, I attended the thanksgiving service, but I could not avoid appreciating that God, in his infinite wisdom would simultaneously be receiving well-earned thanks from both sides. Somewhere in his Elysian rafters Batt must have laughed.

We reached Alexandria on the 17th, and the fleet licked its wounds after what had been an undoubted defeat, and a serious blow to the relief of Malta and the United Kingdom's Mediterranean strategy. Two supply ships did succeed in reaching Malta from the simultaneously timed convoy – Operation Harpoon – which had sailed from Gibraltar. A run ashore was enjoyed by all who were capable. After sampling various well-known watering holes, such as the Excelsior and Pastroudis, and exchanging good-natured ruderies with other destroyer teams led (in their case) uproariously by their commanding officers, ranging from Lt. Commanders even to four-stripe Captains. *Fortune*'s officers, Number One in the lead, enjoyed *haute cuisine* (not a hint of rationing) at Le Petit Coin de France.

As we were leaving after a delicious and gargantuan dinner, I was taken aback when in through the door came shy, dark-eyed Marguerite, who had made such an impression in Alexandia when I was a midshipman, now grown up and escorted by some undeserving Army officer. Soldiers, I decided, had a distinct advantage over peripatetic sailors. She seemed as pleasantly surprised as I was, or so I told myself. There was no opportunity to talk about old times. As ships pass, we exchanged a polite word or two and then went our separate ways. Soon a horse-drawn gharrie with four passengers clip-clopped from Mohammed Ali Square to Number 6 Gate landing stage to the sound of

"We don't want to march with the infantry,
Ride with the cavalry. Fly over Germany.
We are the King's Navee."

Jack would have explored less, or perhaps even more, esoteric and colourful entertainments. Of these there was no shortage in this cosmopolitan pullulating and historic city, of which the ghastly King Farouk had been billed as Play Boy Number One.[8] Mary's House, previously frequented by lieutenants (and above) for tea and other entertainments (unspecified), had not long before been demolished by a direct hit in an air raid. Several clients present on this occasion were gazetted as "killed in Action". It got about later that Stripey had found it necessary to enlist the services of the sickbay to remove his wedding ring from an inappropriate section of anatomy to which it had been unaccountably transferred during this, his only run ashore since leaving Chatham. Sooty returned in a wheelbarrow.

What the captain did with himself nobody knew. We were too tired to care.[9]

Sooty's Return

Chapter 13

Honk

To accomplish his object Ahab must use tools, and of all the tools used in the shadow of the moon, men are most apt to get out of order.

Moby Dick. *Herman Melville*

According to Socrates – "The commander must know how to get his men their rations and every other kind of stores needed for war. He must have imagination to originate plans, practical sense and energy to carry them through. He must be observant, untiring, shrewd, kindly and cruel; simple and crafty, a watchman and a robber; lavish and miserly; generous and stingy; rash and conservative. All these and many other qualities natural and acquired, he must have. He should also as a matter of course, know his tactics, for a disorderly mob is no more of a fighting force than a heap of building material a house."

After eight months Jack, although unlikely to have much interest in Greek philosophy, showed what he thought about his captain quite openly without too obviously breaking the regulations. A penchant for shooting seagulls from the bridge at sea did nothing for his popularity. Sailors years ago liked to imagine that seabirds contained the souls of dead mariners, – some wags said "of chief stokers". It was as well that he was no marksman. Later, when *Fortune* sailed into southern seas and was accompanied by a wandering albatross, Fred the Gunner contrived to land the ship's .22 rifle on the authority of an obscure order on small bore weapon inspection.

The two professionally excellent leading signalmen differed in character. Hannam went about his work cheerfully and without fuss. Nightingale had red hair and was an aggressive "sea lawyer". If he survived the war he could have gone far in a militant trade union. One day he came into the chart house with a signal showing the half yearly officers' promotions, Lt. Commander to Commander and so on, just received and eagerly awaited by the captain. "Thought you had better see this first," he said, then added, "our's isn't on it. Pity. Be glad to get rid of him."

I was taken aback by this remark, even though I privately agreed. I told Nightingale that it was improper and flouted all the rules. "Oh, that's all right, sir," he replied cheerfully. "You can't do anything about it, as there ain't no witness. I'll just deny I ever said it."

I had listened to all sorts of sailors' moans, "drips" and grumbles, some sensible, some not. Midshipmen got a feel for the well-told yarn, spun by the coxswain of the launch or the corporal of the gangway. But the approach adopted by Nightingale was certainly unusual. I told him rather pompously that he would hear shortly from the Yeoman of Signals and

Leading Signalman Hannam

that what he had said was not in accordance with the regulations for stating a complaint. He laughed sardonically. I realised that he attributed my superior (to his) rank and position to undeserved privilege. Even if this contained an element of truth, it was not an attitude reflected in the ship's company.

On speaking to the Yeoman, loyal and newly rated up Petty Officer Cromwell, I sensed that he, though first class at his job, was disturbed by his subordinate's plausibility, eloquence and superficial legal knowledge. I relayed all this unhappily to the First Lieutenant. "Alert the bolshie Nightingale," he said, "of the consequences if he is formally charged with singing this sort of song. No witness needed. He will be for the high jump." This put a stopper on Nightingale, who without in any way diminishing his professional expertise, confined himself from then on to what the coxswain referred to as "dumb insolence", but it was in effect an open display of lower deck feeling.

The disagreeable chore of censoring the ship's company's letters home was also revealing, because operational security, not innuendo, was the only criterion for scissors. Geography being forbidden, there was nothing one could write about except each other. Officers were trusted to censor their own letters. I got round this by not writing any – a selfish and idle solution. Apart from an occasional postcard, my father and mother had to assume, not having heard otherwise, that I was still alive. Many of our sailors were on "Hostilities Only" engagements. They were here to fight for their country, either as volunteers or conscripts – although the last had opted specifically for the Navy as opposed to Army, Airforce or coal mines, the other options. Interest in promoting their C.O.'s advancement was likely to be limited, unless of course it hastened his departure.

Meanwhile, their families were at the receiving end of the Blitz[1] – and also severely rationed for food and clothing. *Fortune* being manned from Chatham, many of her company were Londoners, their families taking the worst beating. Even so, I cannot remember a single occasion when the C.O. chatted up one of his sailors. I suspect he did not know how to. Leadership as a subject, if it was specifically taught before the war at the Royal Naval College, had passed him by.[2] He lacked humanity.

The light touch eluded him. His eccentricities were of a different order to those perpetrated by other destroyer types such as: M, who dived off the floating dock at Scapa Flow at midnight wearing only his luxuriant black beard; B, who was reputed to receive telepathic instructions from his wife on which way to alter course when successfully fighting German E boats; P, who painted the deck of his bridge red for the same reason as

Victory's surgeon his cockpit; N, a gallant but short-sighted officer, who refused to open fire till he himself could see the enemy; D who played the bagpipes because he thought it might encourage troops to embark with alacrity at Dunkirk; W, who took up knitting and filled the bridge with fathoms of woollen scarf, which his wife subsequently chopped into suitable lengths; or even K, who rushed up the bridge ladder with his sou'wester on back to front, complaining that the time of sunrise was wrong. Besides, they compensated by their professionalism.

The officers kept their opinions to themselves, except that is for Philip Archer-Shee, who was openly disloyal when discretion allowed. As a peacetime R.N.V.R. and a nephew of the original Winslow Boy, he granted himself a dispensation to behave entirely to his own, always very civilised, satisfaction.[3] His observations were entertaining, usually coded and thus designed to be unintelligible to an outsider. He commented on the low standard of certain unnamed R.N. officers, who had been given, for no known reason, sea command for which it was obvious that they were not fit.

The Third Lieutenant, Matthews, also a peacetime R.N.V.R., died a thousand deaths in charge of the ship's office, where his duties included serving up the ship's correspondence, both incoming and outgoing. He regularly suffered the fate of the classic messenger on delivery of an unpopular message. Although surprisingly philosophical, he was a nervous person. I had seen him screwing himself up to go in to see the C.O., and later his hunted expression on emerging. He became adept at mislaying, recycling or ditching any correspondence that threatened to disturb a peaceful existence.

The inadequate young doctor had been replaced by confident Surgeon Lieutenant Kenneth Martin, R.N.V.R. This was a welcome change. He was fun and also helped us with extra-mural activities such as cryptography, to avoid which his predecessor had gone to great lengths, quoting the Hague convention. With little or no sickness to cure, not even gonorrhoea (lack of opportunity), how our first doctor had occupied himself was a mystery.

We knew that Jack referred to his captain as "Screaming Skull". Dislike of the master had become the bond that cemented those on board into one company, an unorthodox expedient contrasting somewhat with what is officially recommended. Sailors differentiated then between "Proper Bastards" and "Right Bastards" when referring to certain types of officer. There was a glimmer of approval for the first category. None for the second in which he found himself.

The captain from the outset never disguised dislike of his second-in-command, thus denying himself wise advice. He did not appreciate the enormous contribution that Michael Morris made in seamanship, leadership and sense of fun. Lacking the last quality himself made it worse. He was an explicit example of: "An R.N.R. officer is a seaman trying to be a gentleman. An R.N.V.R. officer is a gentleman trying to be a seaman. An R.N. officer is neither, trying to be both." He did not show evidence of an educated taste in music, art or literature. K.R. & A.I. seemed to be his Bible and his prop – about the only book visible in his cabin.

Passing into the Navy at thirteen, the normal age for Dartmouth, rather than the seventeen-year-old Special Entry Scheme, he survived, presumably by hard labour, what must have been for him an ordeal at the R.N. College without making friends or being rewarded for any achievement. Considered an oddity by contemporaries, the experience could not have been much fun. His nickname was Honk.[4] Schoolboy nicknames stick, so this was now occasionally and improperly used in the ship as an irreverent abbreviation. Instead of saying that the "old man" or "father" – usual expressions – wanted one on the bridge, it would be: "Pilot, wake up! Honk is shouting for you."

His track record remained a mystery. Unlike most sailors, who exaggerate the magnificence or otherwise of previous vessels, he was silent about his past. Success had presumably eluded him, but he must have scraped by in a series of undemanding peacetime jobs. Promotion to the rank of Lt. Commander was automatic. His interest in the ladies seemed nothing out of the usual, but evidently went unrewarded. At the outset of war he married an Austrian immigrant, who promptly walked out, informing him, he said, that she had gone for wedding bells only to acquire a British passport.

In blue uniform he was invariably well-tailored by Messrs Gieves, masters of creating a military figure from unlikely material. But his appearance deteriorated in the tropics, where we all wore regulation, none too well-fitting, issue khaki shorts with sandals, and went shirtless. He was paunchy and his skin was piebald in light and dark patches like a lizard.[5] When he joined me to pore over some detail on the chart table, I instinctively shuddered. He lacked charm.

By now he had also given up any attempt to get close to his officers. He had tried. There was at first a tricky period when the ship arrived in harbour. He would descend on each of us in turn with an invitation to go ashore with him. This experience proved to be one that no one wished to repeat. He was awkward, unable to communicate and humourless apart from schoolboy-type jokes. The upshot was that, as soon as the ship berthed, we all became immersed in terribly important duties. He was not a loner from choice. This arose from his personality.

His negative effect on senior officers was predictable. We dreaded each official call that he made on one of these, and in this activity he was indefatigable. The result was predictable. *Fortune* went to sea the next day. With the exception of the genial and understanding Bill Beloe, already described, and an impossible role model, he was never one of the team when other destroyer captains got together on rare and usually alcoholic occasions. *Fortune*'s switch from one fleet to another and her ultimate employment on mundane, yet essential, single ship duties may have been chance, but could have resulted from this reputation. "Pass the parcel" was the name of the game.

He had a short fuse, not that this is uncommon in the Royal Navy. But his eyes would flare and his face become dark when something angered him. My position remained embarrassingly different from that of the other officers and ship's company, I was not shouted at. He accepted without question my inexperienced, and sometimes flawed, advice and navigational computations. This blind trust resulted in my double-checking all calculations to avoid disaster. I worried, and even had some nightmares in case my good luck should peter out. I had become indispensable for coastal pilotage as much as for deep sea astro-navigation and operational staff work. Electronic navigational systems were not yet with us. The result was that to save time I pushed my luck and just went ahead and made decisions, which should have been made by the captain. No repercussions resulted, either in public or private.

I suppose that even as a beginner I filled a void in his repertoire, inexplicable in someone who had reached his rank. His reliance on my eyesight at night, as with a sextant, was another factor. This apparent special treatment of a junior officer could have made me unpopular with the others. That this did not happen was entirely due to their good nature. They also may have noticed that, although never sworn at, I was also never granted even a "well done" – not that I deserved or expected praise for just getting by. When I proffered advice, which turned out to be not as good as it should have been, he appeared not to notice.

Year after year without recognition must have created in Honk an ambition. I now realised that *Fortune*'s Ahab was obsessed, but his quarry was no Moby Dick. His goal was simply the acquisition of a small ration of fame – a Mention in Despatches, a medal for distinguished service, promotion to commander with "brass hat", or perhaps just a signal from a senior officer saying "manoeuvre well executed", anything at all; even the last appeared to be as elusive as the captain of the *Pequod*'s great white whale.

Sadly his ambition was thwarted daily by mistakes for which he was certain that someone else was responsible. To others he appeared accident-prone. In his own eyes he was a victim, conspired against by the world, fighting to prove his worth in the face of general opposition. Actions motivated by the best of intentions fell apart in his hands.

Lack of common sense, and insensitivity towards others joined with obsession to cover up – even when the outcome was absurd. Dodges and delusions were the order of the day. This had, off Gibraltar, required fudging the analysis of substandard gunnery and torpedo exercises so as to display an optimum result as opposed to the awful actuality. With the fleet at full wartime stretch, no staff officer bothered to study these and in any case my untutored fiddles were unlikely to fool anyone.

Otherwise lacking in flair or ability, Honk rejoiced in just one surprising aptitude. Although not able to secure the ship to a buoy without a great deal of shouting, he handled the ship competently when going alongside a jetty or another ship in harbour. These events were fast and consistently good. He even showed off, irritating Number One by leaving the bridge before the order of "Haul taut and belay", which indicates that the ship is properly secured. No time was wasted. Jack will forgive his captain much for this, particularly when other ships in company are still backing and filling off their berths, while he is already across the gangway. Honk made no allowance, when manoeuvring, as a professional should have done, for a breakdown or mistake in the engineroom, and somehow always got away with it by the skin of his teeth and a massive application of horsepower.

In the open sea his performance was parlous, mainly through lack of judgement, commonsense, or any flair for tactics or feel for weather. This was exacerbated by anxiety to impress any senior officer in the offing. The result was usually the reverse, as on the occasion when we fired dummy torpedoes at *Indomitable* off Aden. He was an exponent of a routine jest recollected from peacetime competitive inter-ship evolutions, "Do something, boy! Doesn't matter what you do, as long as you *do* something."

Loyalty of a grudging sort kept all this disagreeable and disturbing knowledge within "the family". I could not like the man, but I did feel sorry for him. Sea command is by its nature a solitary occupation. Melville's Ahab and Barrie's caricature, the dreaded Captain Hook, were also alone as they tangled one with a whale and the other a crocodile.

Noah, a more balanced conservationist, who knew that two and two resulted in more than four, found this out before them. With so many hang-ups, and unable to make friends or communicate with his officers or Jack, *Fortune*'s captain must have been lonely indeed.

Chapter 14

Albert

Tragedy and Comedy are essentially the same, and they should be written by the same authors.

Socrates

Several of us went to see our two wounded engineroom chief petty officers in the military hospital in Alexandria. They were cheerful, typically splendid senior ratings, and only too glad to rejoin the following morning. We were escorted to a huge ward where the survivors of a destroyer

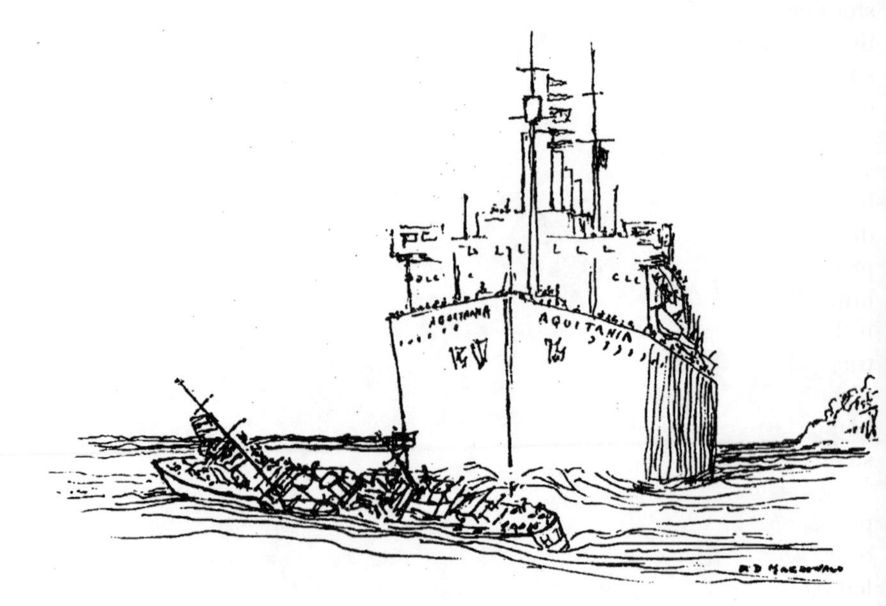

(probably *Hasty*) sunk during Operation *Vigorous* were lying in two rows of beds. Their faces and arms were black and resembled charcoal golliwogs, the terrible consequence of being burnt by oil fuel. The contrast with the pristine whiteness of clean sheets was gross and disturbing. I realised then how necessary it was to be able to swim under water from a sinking ship to avoid the flames, and wondered how good the doctors might be at giving these poor sailors their faces back.

The following day we sailed from Alexandria independently for the Suez Canal, which on this occasion was transited without incident. The canal pilots were all European with not a single Egyptian among them. This one was British. He sat smoking a cigar with its band on, while the coxswain steered the ship down the middle – an easy life. This profitable sinecure, and some other myths about the supposed incompetence of Egyptians, were bowled out years later when Nasser nationalised the Canal.

At Aden *Fortune* became one of four destroyers required to escort *Newcastle* to Mombasa, sailing on 27 June. The 10,000 ton 6-inch gun cruiser had no bows, these having been removed by a torpedo during Operation *Vigorous*. She now needed to make a long, difficult and slow sternboard under her own power across the Indian Ocean in the teeth of the monsoon. I remember unfairly teasing the Yeoman of Signals by suggesting that the screening diagram, because the main body was proceeding stern first, would need to be applied backwards.

But something had happened. More wheel than usual was needed to steer even in still water. In the heavy seas running as the small force headed for Cape Gardafui and the Horn of Africa, it became increasingly difficult to maintain any course without the assistance of main engine and propellers. Naturally I reported this to the captain, who either had not himself detected the phenomenon or more probably had chosen to ignore it. He maintained that it was all due to the bad weather. This was of course transparent nonsense. I suggested, having discussed it with the First Lieutenant, that the rudder could have been disturbed by a near miss from a bomb during our recent duty as Luftwaffe target ship, and the containing steel plates loosened from the frame.

Steering and station keeping were now far from easy. Large impulses of propeller were needed to start a turn. A zigzag had been ordered throughout. This last was a tremendous strain on the engineroom department, now led by the Chief Engineroom Artificer, because of the continuous revolution variations demanded on one engine to point the ship in the right direction on every leg of the zigzag every few minutes. On the bridge we gave up using the ineffective wheel, unless of course to humour the captain when he was present. He still refused to accept that there was anything wrong, brushing aside argument to the contrary. It gradually emerged that he was anxious in case his superiors might think that he had run the ship aground somewhere. As his navigator I was naturally miffed at such an implied criticism of my daily effort, particularly as Luck had so far been on our side. He was convinced that such a suspicion would count against his career prospects. "Promotionitis" is a debilitating affliction.

The high wind and heavy seas often meant that to take up her appointed station the ship had to turn the longest way round, that is by more than 180 degrees. The reason for such an unusual manoeuvre, not being known to the screen commander, *Fortune* became the recipient of even more than her share of rude signals for eccentric station keeping. To H 70, "What are you doing?" To which there was no known answer. Our master preferred his officer of the watch to be considered incompetent than to come clean about the rudder.

We staggered along at six knots, the maximum speed that the crippled *Newcastle* could maintain. The weather, which was foul, got worse and the speed made good diminished. The ship rolled heavily as she laboured with the monsoon-driven sea, dark olive and black, on the beam. The wave-washed upper deck was impassable and the ship battened down for safety. The compass was constantly encrusted with salt. Once again Jack saw the eerie green glow of St. Elmo's Fires on the yardarms. Once again he wondered what this could mean. On 30th June, when it was clearly hopeless to continue in the prevailing weather, the group turned back for Aden.

Subsequently *Fortune* was sailed independently to Kilindini, the fleet anchorage close by Mombasa, arriving on 7th July. This was an opportunity to arrange for a fleet diver to inspect the rudder, something that our late engineer officer would have organised surreptitiously off his own bat. Warships had not yet acquired the benefit of their own complemented free-swimming divers. (It was not till 1944 that I had an opportunity to qualify as a diver.) But the captain would not hear of it, nor was anyone keen to take a quick look and end up as lunch for a shark, or be questioned by the captain, – proportionately equivalent dangers. After oiling we sailed to rendezvous *Aquitania*, the famous old Cunard liner that *Valiant* had escorted across the Atlantic in 1939, now employed as a fast, and for that reason unescorted, troop carrier to cover the last and most vulnerable part of her voyage to Diego Suarez.

I had become fascinated by "shooting" the stars and planets, as well as the sun, to find the ship's position. What was only a routine calculation magically linked myself with a magnificent glittering star, so far away that the light I saw left it before the Romans invaded Britain. On 16 July my sight book records the altitudes of Rigel, Achernar, Fomalhaut, Venus and Betelgeuse taken in dawn sights. Often these morning and evening events involved just a fleeting glimpse of a Tinkerbell flicker through whirling clouds over a bleary horizon. There was also the genuine excitement felt on making a first landfall as each conspicuous mark, identified previously from the "Pilot" (Sailing Directions), popped up or perhaps did not pop up . . .

On 19 July we brought *Aquitania*, 45,647 tons, stuffed with troops, towards Orija Pass, the entrance to Diego. Our C.O. chose, for some reason that he did not explain, to station his ship, the sole escort, for the approach close ahead of the massive four-funnelled liner, while at the same time carrying out a broad zigzag from one bow to the other, although he was well aware of our own defective steering. With the troopship doing twenty knots, our own speed had to be greater to maintain station. This made the manoeuvre useless for Anti-Submarine defence, and because we were approaching shallow water and were steering by main engines, it was also dangerous. From the huge liner's troop decks these manoeuvres presumably looked purposeful to the uninitiated, and certainly exciting.

There was a heavy following sea running towards the entrance as soundings (of depth) became less. The ship felt like a car with bald tyres on a skid pan. She was clearly unmanoeuvrable. As *Fortune* crossed close ahead of the splendid liner towering above, all these adverse factors combined and bore the ship down on her beam ends in a spectacular broach to. She slithered on her port side, just squeezing out from under *Aquitania*'s knife-like stem looming overhead. Being daylight, this interesting event was visible to all. It frightened the officers on the bridge of *Aquitania*, but not half as much as it frightened us. (In the North Atlantic three months later on 20th October, R.M.S. *Queen Mary* carved her escort, the light cruiser *Curacoa*, in half with many dead.)[1]

The captain for once said nothing. He retired further into himself, communicating even less except for what was required in the normal business of the day. However, he at last agreed to an inspection of the rudder, and this was asked for by immediate signal. This was the only occasion that the ship broke wireless silence at sea throughout the commission.

Fortune sailed independently via the Seychelles and the One and a Half Degree channel through the Maldives to Colombo where in dry dock, as expected, all was revealed. What remained of her rudder proved to be only the frame, a sort of inverted music stand. The containing metal plates were missing, a souvenir of Operation *Vigorous*.

It felt strange to be again in what were now curiously peaceful waters from which so recently the Eastern Fleet, having suffered a hammering by the Japanese, had then ignominiously, but wisely retreated. But then so had the Japanese. On 13th August, after repairs were complete, we left again for Kilindini to rejoin the fleet, everyone having enjoyed a short taste of the bright lights in an elegantly peaceful town – swimming pools, lawns, Gaulle Face hotel bar, almost affordable semi-precious stones, unobtainable Wrens, good beer and agreeable climate. One could not avoid noticing the built-in antipathy between superior, arrogant, pale Dravidian Ceylonese and energetic, deep brown immigrant Tamil. The smell of camphor, sandal wood and green tea reminded me of Java. The all too recent air raid inflicted on Colombo by the Japanese might never have happened. Jack returned from his unprogrammed run ashore more or less on time and without any trouble, apart from a thick head the next day.

But we had embarked, or more accurately shanghaied, a passenger. Almost at the last moment the Wardroom messman, reacting to the captain's predilection for guest nights, and perhaps assisted by a dram or two of palm wine, returned on board accompanied by two locals bearing between them a turtle of more than normal magnificence and dimension. Deposited to its indignation the wrong way up, literally turned turtle on the iron deck, its paddles flapped helplessly to and fro.

Not long afterwards Albert was comfortably afloat in the rubber dinghy from which we had rescued the Beaufighter crew in the Mediterranean, now secured among the depth charges and topped up with seawater. He paddled round his private pool in a dignified way, sampling herrings-in-tomato-sauce, tots of rum and other delicacies considered appropriate by the ship's company, who had rapidly adopted him. This introduced a difficulty. The captain had been promised an aldermanic feast, but the sailors were by now devoted to Albert, who had become a personality.

One enchanted starlit evening, zig-zagging somewhere between the Maldives and Zanzibar, the dreaded occasion arrived. The Wardroom loyally pretended to enjoy a disgusting concoction knocked up by Sooty with some assistance from the cookery school manual and half a bottle of Grand Marnier. Meanwhile Albert, who after sunset had been given a surreptitious "float test", was beating the open turtle record home.

Chapter 15

Edge of the Volcano

Without discipline is well planned and strictly supported, a military corps, or a ship's crew are no better than a disorderly mob.

Kempenfelt, 1779

On arrival at Kilindini, we berthed for the first and indeed only time on the destroyer depot ship flying the flag of Rear Admiral (Destroyers) Eastern Fleet. She towered above us, noisy with ventilation fans and workshop machinery. Shortly afterwards a messenger asked me to report to our First Lieutenant in his cabin. This was unusual. I was surprised to find Philip Archer-Shee and Porny Mathews already there. As the engineer officer was dead, the four lieutenants (I had just been routinely promoted) present were, apart from the Warrant Gunner (T) and the Surgeon Lieutenant R.N.V.R., the full complement of ship's officers. Other fleet destroyers sometimes had at least one extra officer under training, together with a midshipman or two.

Number One appeared to be, if not uneasy, at least not his normally relaxed self. He explained, speaking quietly, and choosing his words carefully that he had called us together, because in his opinion the ship and all those in her were continually being placed at risk by the captain's irrational decisions. It was not that he was just eccentric, after all the Navy was accustomed to eccentricity, but actually out of his mind. He mentioned a number of incidents, the most recent being his absolute refusal to report, or even investigate, the obviously damaged rudder, culminating in the hair-raising near miss with *Aquitania*. We remembered only too well the "gun shy dog"; leaving Gibraltar; a refusal to half mast the ensign for Chief's burial; the regular instant rages, screams and shouts

aimed indiscriminately. There had been occasions when he had sensed that some of the ship's company were on the point of refusing a duty, or staging a major demonstration. This was alarming. He appreciated that our present meeting was in itself irregular, but then the circumstances that occasioned it were extraordinary.

He added that what made it difficult to take independent action, was that the doctor, who should have been as aware as everyone else of the C.O.'s state of mind, positively refused to consider drafting a medical report on him. Whether or not he had taken a reading of a senior member of the medical mafia he did not know. His predecessor had been terrified by the captain, at the same time wrestling with Hippocrates as well as the Hague and Geneva conventions. If mythology contains a god of common sense, his influence was sorely needed at this moment.

Without beating about the bush, Archer-Shee summed up that, while everyone on board realised that the man was a nut case and should be got rid of, the problem was how to achieve his removal. I suspected that he had persuaded Number One to call the meeting in the first place, because to Michael Morris anything remotely resembling such a grave defiance of the Laws of the Navy would normally have been anathema. Michael then said that he had searched the regulations in vain for guidance. There was no drill for such a situation, nor any flotilla staff available with particular, or inside, knowledge of the ship or responsibility for her, to turn to for advice. *Fortune* was as usual detached from her administrative authority, and indeed at the time no one was quite sure who this ethereal being actually was.

We were clearly in very deep water. Struggling to recollect my rudimentary knowledge of the Naval Discipline Act, I had a distinct feeling that what I was being invited to take part in was a mutinous assembly, albeit for the best of intentions, with such, as it is said, the way to hell is paved. I thought suddenly of Fletcher Christian, Bligh and the *Bounty*, not to mention the aftermath. I was also aware that the ship had been put at risk by our C.O. on a number of occasions for reasons that were irrational and in my view unforgivable. This was quite apart from the disturbing point made by Number One on the state of discipline.

I suggested diffidently that one solution might be for Number One to go over now to the depot ship and see the Admiral's secretary. This presumably most knowledgeable officer should be able to advise on correct procedure, if there was one, to deal with our predicament.

Number One was not enthusiastic. He maintained that his credibility in such a unique situation would appear weak because of his limited service in the Royal Navy, the Surgeon Lieutenant's refusal to give support, and the lack of tangible evidence outwith the ship of the captain's mental instability. *Fortune*, after all, had accomplished every operational directive in the Atlantic, the Mediterranean and in the Eastern Fleet. What went on within her was not public knowledge.

Archer-Shee pressed eloquently and at length for something to be done before disaster befell. Mathews, all for a quiet life, agreed. I was torn, deciding between which was the greater cowardice in the circumstances: to stay and (as I thought at the time) subsequently face a court martial for being party to a mutinous assembly (with appropriate disgrace) or feebly to leave the meeting and be an accessory to a horrible disaster yet to come.

I decided to stay, but was apprehensive and unsure whether this was wise either for the ship or, in the last resort, for myself personally, as a very junior hopeful on the bottom rung of a career in the Royal Navy.

Nevertheless, I agreed with the others that it would be in the interest of the fleet for the captain to be relieved of the command of *Fortune*, preferably unobtrusively for medical reasons, as soon as possible. I felt by this time no loyalty to the captain as a person, although sorry for him. Meanwhile, paradoxically I remained loyal to the office he filled. This was a conflict that I found disturbing and at times difficult to cope with. We also knew from experience that as a leader in battle he was about as much use as Jack's proverbial "fart in a gale of wind". By this time the cabin was thick with cigarette smoke – a blend of Balkan Sobranie (First Lieutenant), Philip Morris (Archer-Shee) and Capstan Navycut (Mathews). I felt that I needed fresh air.

Number One, who had been mulling over our various contributions, then said that he would be prepared to go over to the flagship and consult the admiral's personal staff, but only if we all went with him. After some further discussion a compromise was reached. He would see the Flag Secretary on his own and, perhaps subsequently, the Admiral, if this was the advice that he received. We would accompany him onboard the depot ship, but remain available within reach only in case we were needed to provide supporting evidence, a sort of Greek chorus. It was all most irregular.

So it was that the four lieutenants, two R.N. and two R.N.V.R., in our cleanest white tropical rig, best shoulder straps and in order of seniority, an unlikely and somewhat ludicrous crocodile of mutineers – the most junior feeling slightly sick – trooped over the brow connecting *Fortune* with the towering ship alongside. It felt like walking the plank. Philip Archer-Shee alone was not in the slightest bit concerned about the course that we had embarked on. I admired his insouciance, but also knew that he had not much to lose, and anyway had inherited (by way of his family's already referred to legal and theatrical example) no great reverence for naval judicial proceedings.

We arrived eventually at the Admiral's cabin flat, a glittering holy place reflecting polish, brightwork and tablets of stone. An armed Royal Marine sentry, immaculate in khaki drill order and red hat band, was posted in front of the ship's rifle, bayonet and cutlass racks, relics of past and deterrent to future mutinies – as I well knew. I suddenly wished that I was somewhere else.

After a pause Number One, showing some hesitation, raised his arm to knock, the first and only time I had seen this stalwart personality in any way put out. The door was decorated with much tiddly ropework. Emblazoned in scarlet and white, a rear admiral's flag, St. George's Cross decorated with two red balls, flew above the legend "Admiral's Secretary". We waited in suspense. It seemed to me that an age passed. No one said anything. Number One's arm returned limply to his side. We looked from one to another. There was a further painful moment. Somehow, having set off as a band of gallant crusaders, we were diminishing visibly both in confidence and stature into a bunch of shifty conspirators. We could have been in a cathedral. The silence was monumental. Then, without further ado, four demoralised individuals turned together as a body and shuffled back across the narrow brow to their own ship. This humiliating non-event was not discussed, or ever mentioned again, by any of those who took part. As ever, drama and farce were indistinguishable in *Fortune*.

We had been beaten by a system that was beyond our understanding. We had perched precariously on the rim of a smoking volcano. None of us had sufficient experience to appreciate that our situation might not have been unique. Mental breakdown of some warship captains due to stress of battle in a very long war does happen. Senior officers (and medicos) are geared up to handle such an event and make allowances for special circumstances. The important difference here was that our C.O.'s irrational behaviour was not brought on initially, although possibly aggravated, by stress of war. In harbour *Fortune*'s captain would, if called upon to defend himself formally, put on an impressive performance as a smartly turned out, standard professional, Dartmouth-trained Royal Naval officer doing his utmost, although much handicapped by a motley "Hostilities" crew of less than average competence and more than average disloyalty. He would have quite correctly drawn attention to the fact that his ship had undeniably met every one of her operational duties and that included when under enemy fire. Perhaps it was inevitable, and as well for everybody, that this protest fizzled out.

Nevertheless, when seen in considerable retrospect (that is half a century later), something indefinable seemed to have happened at that moment. And whatever this was, it did have an effect even though imperceptible at the time. We had, without knowing it, surmounted a watershed, coincidentally almost half way through a commission, the length of which we did not as yet know. It was only very gradually that this sea change would become evident to those of us serving, not without justifiable anxiety, in *Fortune*.

Later that evening Stripey could be heard relating the Death of Nelson, a lugubrious but popular performance, with vulgar variations, outside the fo'c's'le locker, his spade-like fingers deftly tucking the strands of a three and a half inch wire rope splice as if they were silk.

Chapter 16

Figgy Duff

Grog, the sailor's best friend, and the main support of the British Navy.

Satirical pamphlet, eighteenth century

Englishmen, and more especially seamen, love their bellies above anything else.

Samuel Pepys

There was a further change of mood within *Fortune*. Perhaps this was due to a reaction from the impact of Operation *VIGOROUS* and the close run thing with *Aquitania*. Perhaps it was just an adjustment of tempo from the hurly burly of the Mediterranean to the unbelievable deep peace of the Indian Ocean in and around Mombasa and Madagascar. This had become a wartime backwater. There was of course much frenetic activity as she was only one unimportant unit among something like three flotillas of destroyers, Commodore (D) S. H. T. Arliss, that provided an anti-submarine screen for the Eastern Fleet. No known threat existed from hostile air or surface forces. It was a curious example of a "fleet in being", since what its purpose was we did not know, the Japanese having departed to the Pacific to fight the Americans.

Being wise after the event, the whole shooting match would have been more profitably employed escorting convoys in the Atlantic, where the sinking of merchant shipping by U-boats had reached astronomic proportions (the total loss for 1942 was over six million tons), mainly due to shortage of escorts.[1]

Whatever the reason, the atmosphere within *Fortune* resembled a sluggish mixture which chemistry could turn volatile. It was not easy to

provide diversions. Sports facilities did not exist. Our C.O., lacking sensitivity, and therefore understandably from his particular angle, appreciated that here was a splendid opportunity to impress the boss. *Fortune* would outshine her consorts in smartness of appearance and her willingness to be up front at all times, no matter what: a policy summed up in the ancient naval adage "attitude is the art of gunnery".

Number One, practical and scrupulous in his habits, had maintained the ship and her weapon systems with efficiency and pride. Everything worked, sometimes miraculously. His ship husbandry was beyond criticism. Similarly the Engineroom Department had never let us down, and was not likely to do so. There were, though, two constraints to the instant achievement of the captain's desire for a pretty ship. As already indicated, one was that priorities had so far been correctly dictated by operational requirements; sinking the enemy and remaining afloat against all odds being of more importance than paintwork. The other was that Number

One, because of his previous career in the Merchant and not the Royal Navy, admitted only too readily that he was to some extent ignorant of what it was his captain really wanted. It would also seem that he did not get much, if any, guidance.

By this stage of the war, any semblance of peacetime nicety of appearance among fleet destroyers had been abandoned unless it stemmed as a consequence of good seamanship. Ships were painted drab grey or camouflaged in various tones, stripes and angular shapes with the object of confusing the U-boat. There was even a style known as Mountbatten Pink. Wartime paint lacked body and often blew off at sea. "Tiddly" ropework, Turk's Heads, brass brightwork and decoration of widgets with white, blue and gold leaf were out. Rust was chipped and red lead took its place.

It was probably true that our upper deck and ship's side were not up to the standard of much newer J, K, L and Hunt class destroyers, some with galvanised and so rust-proof hulls and superstructure. *Fortune*'s guard rail stanchions were not all as straight as they should have been, a consequence of broaching on two occasions. Her funnels were often brown or

yellow due to hard steaming in heavy seas, a "salt-caked smokestack effect" pleasurable in the eyes of a poet or artist, but not to naval officers. Although there were no Irish pendants (loose lines flapping in the breeze), I suspect that at this stage *Fortune* looked distinctly scruffy, but so did other destroyers of her vintage.

It was also the case that the ship's company as a whole, and not just those on Hostility Only engagements, believed, not without reason, that they were there to fight a war, not to "show the flag". The C.O.'s ukase was tactless in its timing. For seven months at sea Jack had been in Two Watch Defence Stations (i.e. half closed up and half stood down), four hours on watch and four hours off, when not at Action Stations (i.e. everybody closed up). Now, with a reduced threat, less of the armament needed to be manned constantly. In the captain's view there was ample spare labour available to titivate, and the time available to do it.

A warship's complement is based on her ability to man all her weapons and sensors in action, together with provision for damage control, maintenance of machinery and weapons and continuing propulsion. Because, before the advent of automation, such activities were labour intensive, there had been in the piping days of peace a need to "occupy" an excess of people in addition to time spent on training, exercises and organised games. The belief existed, and not without reason, that the devil makes work for idle hands. These traditional factors naturally influenced the thought processes of our captain, who quite unusually for one in his profession had no contact with Jack, or, it would seem, any understanding of him – or for that matter of his officers.

My memory of the event that I describe is not as clear as it should be for a number of reasons. I was not personally involved, except latterly as a bemused spectator, not at all sure whether he is suddenly about to become a highly involved participant. The account is therefore fitted together as a jigsaw of coloured impressions gathered half a century ago and now fuzzy at the edges. Pieces may have been touched with the edge of the brush, but with the minimum of artistic licence, knowing, as I did, all the characters on the canvas only too well.

The ship had anchored the day before at Diego Suarez, the Scapa Flow of French Madagascar, in company with the Battle Squadron, whose nostalgic bugle calls drifted across the water. Despatch boats scurried hither and thither. Red hawks hovered hopefully over the gash chute in expectation of tasty morsels, unavailable in nearby Antisarane, the most impoverished and squalid town that I had ever seen. It was windless and hot. By noon it would be very hot.

The seamen were expecting as usual to work a form of tropical harbour routine. This involved starting earlier in the cool of the morning and finishing the day's work soon after midday, when they went to "dinner", the main meal of the day. Now, to catch up with the "new look", the men were told that they would be fallen in for further work in the afternoon. This did not affect the stokers, who were still watchkeeping, three hours on and six off, or my own communicators for the same reason.

Before dinner at noon the issue of rum was made as usual in accordance with the regulations. For Jack this was the highlight of the day. The "tot" consisted of half a gill of neat rum, which is equal to at least two double whiskies, mixed under an officer's supervision with water in the case of those below the rank of Petty Officer. The mix was called Grog.[2] Customarily knocked back in one gulp, it had in the days of sail gone some way to compensate for the privations of life on board.

Now it helped to digest a menu (their own choice depending on availability of ingredients) consisting of a massive helping of beef stew, boiled potatoes with onions and carrots, if available, known as Pot Mess. A traditional pudding, Figgy Duff, beloved by Jack even more than Baby's Leg (roly-poly suet, boiled in a dish cloth), followed this down. There would have been minor variations, because each mess provided its own amateur "cook" to prepare the meal, taking the dish, labelled for ownership, to the galley for the ship's professional chef to go through the

motions of opening and closing the oven door. This primitive culinary arrangement had existed in small ships since before Nelson's day. Jack actually said he liked it, perhaps because a careful mess could collect some financial discount, referred to as "savings". In a tropically hot messdeck, wreathed in duty free tobacco smoke, such a gastronomic combination must have been some Micky Finn.

Shortly before "Out Pipes" (the warning given five minutes before the order Both Watches of the Hands fall in), Sunny Jim, the Chief Boatswain's Mate, his gold teeth flashing anxiously in the glare of the midday sun, approached Number One and told him that he had heard from the Leading Seamen that the men did not want to work in the afternoon; did not intend to do so; and would not obey the order in any case.

Although Michael Morris had been concerned about such a reaction before, and had referred to his premonition at our abortive and irregular officers' meeting in Kilindini, the actuality must have been a shock. "Spithead, The Nore, *Bounty*, Invergordon, all historic mutinies, now it was *Fortune*'s turn," must have flashed through his mind. "Down Tools, Everybody Out" was not all that uncommon in industry even in wartime, but a mutiny is a mutiny – an unspeakable event in the Royal Navy. It quite upsets Their Lordships and inevitably brings disgrace on everyone in any way connected, however remotely, with it. It also makes a ship useless as a fighting unit and swells the Court Martial Returns, creating a great deal of paperwork.

Number One ordered the men to be fallen in without delay. The order was to be emphasised by the Boatswain's Mate going round the mess-decks piping on his shrill boatswain's call, followed by some jollying along by Sunny Jim. The Petty Officers and most of the Leading Hands obeyed. Many, as usual anticipating the order, appeared, but not one junior rating turned up. Stripey's "yardarm" was clear. His falling in position was the fo'c's'le locker, the "caboosh" where he lived in any

case. This mass refusal to obey an order was without doubt mutiny as defined in the Naval Discipline Act (page 60 above).

I was on my way forward from the Wardroom when I realised with horror what was happening. I felt stunned. Whether or not the sailors had a legitimate complaint, they were totally out of court, as they well knew, in taking the law into their own hands. I wondered how Number One would handle the situation and regain control, because this was an essential first step to rectify a major breakdown in discipline. Whether or not he reported to the captain at this stage I do not know. I suspect that he did not. Indeed, at that time of day our captain would have been visiting other ships, perhaps even the flagship *Resolution*, on one of his many formal calls on senior officers. A further and more peremptory order to "turn to" by the Coxswain, the most senior rating, had been made with no result.

Without hesitation Number One took down the framed copy of the Articles of War from the lobby bulkhead (its message normally absorbed by the ship's company about as much as the small print on an insurance policy). He selected a section, which read:

"MUTINY

> 10. Where mutiny is accompanied by violence, every person subject to this act who shall join therein shall suffer death . . .
> 11. Where a mutiny is not accompanied by violence, the ringleader or ringleaders of such mutiny shall suffer death, or such other punishment as is hereinafter mentioned; and all other persons who shall join such mutiny, or shall not use their utmost exertions to suppress the same, shall suffer imprisonment or such other punishment as is hereinafter mentioned."

He then visited each of the seamans' messdecks in turn, accompanied by the Coxswain, and publicly read out the relevant article. He dwelt specifically on the Draconian punishments meted out by Their Lordships to silly, as he put it, sailors, guilty of such a heinous crime as mutiny in time of war. These, he emphasised with appropriate gravity, included Death. He then returned to the upper deck and ordered the pipe to be made again for both watches of the hands to muster. Throughout this performance he was impressively composed, whatever he may have felt. My heart was in my mouth.

Like badgers emerging cautiously from the cosy gloom of their winter sett, sailor after sailor stumbled onto the iron deck in the burning sunlight.

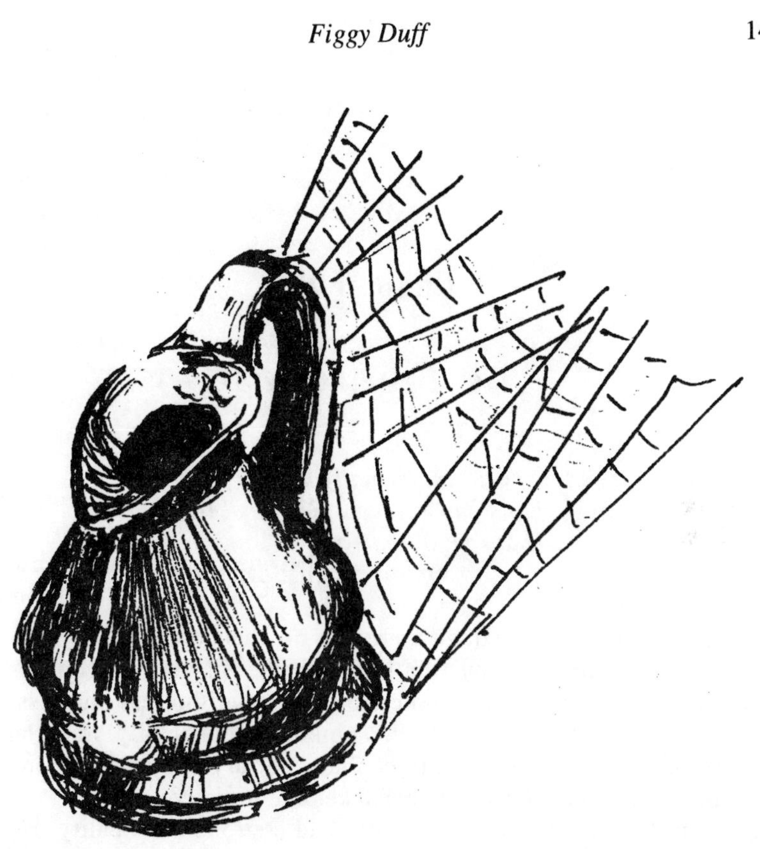

Rubbing their eyes, they stood in an embarrassed line to be detailed off for a variety of mundane cleaning jobs by the Chief Boatswain's Mate. Nobody looked at anyone else. First all took part in an unsolicited head-clearing clockwise trot three times round the upper deck, encouraged by the Gunner's Mate's stentorian "Lef Rai Lef Rai". As the procession passed the fo'c's'le locker, Stripey, ejecting the quid of tobacco that he had been chewing into a spitkid, was heard to chant lugubriously, "Onward Christian Sailors. Not so fast in front."

Fortune's mutiny in Diego Suarez had been stopped by a stalwart officer well short of *Bounty* proportions.[3] It was not recorded in the ship's deck log nor, of course, mentioned in the Report of Proceedings. Figgy Duff came off the menu for about a week. The rum ration was ended twenty-eight years later in 1970, by Act of Parliament.[4]

Chapter 17

The Figurehead

Figurehead. (1) Carving, usually bust or full-length figure, over ship's cut-water. (2) Nominal leader or president without real authority.

Oxford English Dictionary

From about this time, although there was no change in Honk's personality, there was a marked reduction in the number of instant decisions that he made without any evident reflection. We saw him less and less. The reason for this remains a mystery. Thinking about it fifty years later, I believe that the solution can only be that, contrary to what we thought at the time, the good doctor must have taken the initiative.

Surgeon Lieutenant Kenneth Martin had a strong personality. He was no fool. He would have known what Jack thought about his captain through talking to him during routine inspections, inoculations and other occasions for a trip to the sickbay, quite apart from what his sick berth assistant may have told him. More of what nowadays is called counselling would have occurred at this level than any other. He would also be well aware of the officers' opinion, even though the subject was never discussed. It had surprised us all at the time when Number One had said at our recent irregular Lieutenants' meeting that the doctor refused to support his intention to report the situation created by the Captain's instability.

My surmise is that the doctor took advice at this stage from a senior medical officer, either when we were alongside the depot ship or when we were visited by the Fleet Medical Officer, a surgeon captain, for a totally different reason described later. It is possible he told his superior that in his opinion Honk was either a manic depressive or schizoid, or if not

either of these he was sufficiently mentally disturbed to have lost the respect of his officers and ship's company.

The outcome might have been a friendly talk between doctor and captain on some pretext, giving the former the opportunity to ask whether all was well. This could have encouraged Honk to come clean about his internal struggle and difficulties. The advice that he received would, knowing our doctor, not beat about the bush. A warning might have lurked within the velvet glove that handed out friendly advice about relaxation and perhaps some tranquillising pills to control moments in extremis. All this, of course, is unsupported speculation after half a century with no professional expertise.

We did not detect any significant change at the time, but we were not looking out for it. *Fortune* was busy for the remainder of August 1942, together with September and October. The incident at Diego Suarez – and a mutiny is a mutiny even if nipped in the bud – had left an uneasy feeling in its wake. It was as well that there was little time to brood when rushing about screening different units of the fleet from Kilindini to Diego and back, also military convoys converging on the Mediterranean. Then came the assault and capture of Majunga and Tamatave, Vichy French bases in Madagascar, both giving up without a fight. An idea of this activity is indicated on Map B.

Much time was spent at high speed, changing station on the screen and manoeuvring in the dark and line ahead, one and a half cables (300 yards) apart without lights. We ran into bad weather. The sea was lumpier than usual and the chart house resembled an out-of-control hotel lift, colliding first with the roof and then the basement, leaving stomach at the bottom and a headache at the top. A bucket alongside became an essential adjunct. Prewar destroyers were bad seaboats and sometimes suffered damage when driven hard in bad weather.

Jack had now worked out, well before his officers, that it was half time in the ship's commission, though there was no logical way that he could have arrived at this prognostication. From now on, in his optimistic view, we were sliding downhill and almost homeward bound, hurrah! This was arrant nonsense of course, but ultimately it proved to be nearly true. Little difference was made, except that the good ship *Fortune*, however thrown about by Fate, was now considered to have proved herself to be a survivor and thus a lucky ship. Her by now increasingly reclusive captain had become a totem. Disliked and even feared, much in the same way as a primitive tribe worships a carved, and even diabolical, statue on which its future in some mysterious way depends, Jack, understandably superstitious in war, had come to look on Honk, while still an ogre, to be in a strange undetermined way linked to the ship's safe return home. After all, just look at the way *Fortune* had successfully dodged *Indomitable*, *Aquitania* and a shower of high explosives with only one fatal casualty.

This belief uncannily resembled a Polynesian Cargo Cult, a favourite subject in Number One's polyglot repertoire. "Give no trouble; then one dreamy day out of the blue all sorts of goodies will shower down from on high, such as Home Sweet Home, mother's cooking, "all night in", bed and sex." In days of oars and sail a ship's figurehead had also been her totem. In classical times it propitiated a sea deity. It kept a lookout, as do eyes painted on the bows of a Chinese junk or Egyptian felucca. Later, a figurehead's responsibility was supply of good luck. During the battle of The Glorious First of June the *Brunswick*'s figurehead had its cocked hat shot off by a cannon ball. The sailors were so upset that the captain gave them his own hat, which the carpenter nailed on. Any hat, but preferably a civilian bowler, would have been gladly sacrificed by *Fortune* in such a worthy cause.[1]

Chapter 18

Aye Aye

The Wardroom had happily absorbed the new "Chiefy", Harry Duckworth, Acting Warrant Engineer, direct and sensible. His personal contribution was welcome. We had reached the stage when the Old Guard knew each other's stories only too well, so that it was possible to refer to them by numbers to save each other from having to pretend to listen. New blood provided not only new stories, but a new audience.

In the days before quarantine regulations became strict, a variety of small animals added to the quality of life on board. In *Valiant* the Ordinance Engineer kept a tame white rat in his uniform jacket. The Wardroom mascot, Aye Aye, a grey and silver Madagascar lemur about the size of a small squirrel, took to the new "Chief" so much that, when navigating its personal upper Rain Forest – pipes, punkah louvre ventilators, channel plates, asbestos and multiple wiring – in pursuit of cockroaches he would stop directly over Chief's armchair, survey him lovingly with boot black eyes, then drip, drip, drip, followed by curses from the loved one below at the receiving end.

Nocturnal and vegetarian by nature, Aye Aye gradually converted to appearing in the dog watches (late afternoon), and eventually onto the Wardroom table to negotiate an inappropriate breakfast, clutching scraps of bacon and egg in his tiny hands. There was in the ship a shortage of jungle plant life. He was a member of a protected species, so we had no right to keep him there even in relaxed captivity and actually felt guilty about it. But he was a gift from the Senior Nursing sister, Mombasa, to the First Lieutenant for some unspecified service rendered and good for morale, which is an excuse for much in war. One airless tropical night, Aye Aye alighted on Chief's rotating table fan to cool off. We were aroused by piercing shrieks when his woolly tail fouled the axis, rolled up round it

and stopped the system, leaving the little creature spreadeagled across the fan blades. The Eastern Fleet Medical Officer, an important surgeon captain, appeared alongside in the admiral's barge and a flurry of foam, to attend the casualty, who fortunately turned out to be only bruised and sorry for himself. Aye Aye's importance in the pecking order of sick and wounded, I gathered, was due to the fingers of his tiny front paws, which in lemurs structurally resemble those of a man's hand and are thus unique among animals. To the locals of Madagascar, lemurs are an omen of bad luck and were even then on their way to extermination. The Wardroom kept this sensitive intelligence to themselves. Aye Aye was sadly lost overboard soon after, and before a mate could be embarked, who would inevitably have been called No No.

Chapter 19

Soldier Sailor

A diversion was provided by a dummy assault by the Eastern Fleet Destroyer Flotilla to test the defences of Tanganyika against a hypothetical Japanese invasion. *Fortune*'s role was to interdict the road to Dar-es-Salaam from the north. At first light the ship's landing party of "Jolly Jacks", wearing tin hats and green gaiters, armed to the teeth with Lee Enfield rifles and cutlasses, and led by an impressively military Archer-Shee, landed in the motor cutter towing the whaler. Resembling an early

engraving of the relief of Khartoum, they set up a road block, while *Fortune* practised a dummy bombardment, banging off an assortment of fireworks and coloured smoke.

Shortly a stream of important civilians, such as the Chief of Police, the Chief Fire Officer and the Chairman of the Defence Executive Committee, who lived in smart houses in the country some distance to the north of the capital, came whizzing down the road and were promptly taken prisoner by our landing party. This upset them. They maintained that they all had essential duties in the defence of Dar-es-Salaam. How could they be expected to carry these out as prisoners? Town and country would be disorganised. An important exercise, they claimed, was being ruined by dim-witted naval interference.

In due course a platoon of dusky troops emerged guardedly out of the bush, accompanied by a very pink local umpire, who decided by a head count that the Navy should retreat, not paying too much attention to *Fortune*'s simulated naval gunfire support. It was not clear whether the local militia had been briefed that this frolic was only an exercise, according to Archer-Shee, who later put on a breath-taking performance of rolling eyes, ivory teeth and glittering bayonets. It was as well that no one had been issued with live ammunition. It was even more fortunate for sleepy colonial Dar-es-Salaam that *Fortune*'s contribution had not been mounted by the Imperial Japanese Navy.

Chapter 20

The Nancy Brig

Oh, I am a cook and a captain bold,
And the mate of the Nancy Brig,
And a bo'sn tight, and a midship mite,
And the crew of the captain's gig.
Gilbert

The Navy is very good training for an actor.
Rod Steiger

In mid-October the pattern changed abruptly. *Map A*. This created no surprise as nobody ever knew what was in store next. The ship escorted the cruiser *Gambia* and a trooper *Eastern Prince* to Durban. An Admiralty signal had arrived ordering Lieutenant Michael Morris R.N. to return to the U.K. He eventually crossed to St. Johns, Newfoundland, to take command of *Roxborough*, a four-funnel ex-U.S.N. destroyer (one of those primitive old ships Winston Churchill swapped for Bermuda). Her R.N. C.O. had been killed, when the bridge was carried away by an Atlantic wave. The same Admiralty note appointed Lieutenant Philip Archer-Shee, R.N.V.R. forthwith, as First Lieutenant of *Fortune*. There was no mention of any addition to make up numbers, which there should have been. Nor, as far as I knew, did the C.O. ever ask for one.

Philip Archer-Shee was as stunned as Michael Morris was delighted. Years later, Michael told me later than he had occasionally wondered how Archer-Shee managed as Number One. "Philip," he said, "delighted to sit on the fence languidly commenting on how a First Lieutenant should manage his affairs." Michael much enjoyed breaking the news. "Philip nearly passed out," he said, "His reaction was rather similar to that of

some German army type with a soft job in Paris being told he was for the Russian front." I was sad to see Michael go. His humour, steady personality and influence in the ship would be sorely missed. In his laid-back, professional way, he had taught me more than I realised at the time. He was one of the best First Lieutenants that I ever knew, and I have known a great many.

In the event Philip, who was certainly not stupid, disguised most of his anxieties, which stemmed from his horror of the captain's unusual personality, and managed well. He sensibly leaned on the advice of the senior ratings; of Fred, the Gunner, and sometimes, when he was hard pushed, even on mine. He surprised me one day by asking my advice on a non-service matter. Should he, or should he not, propose marriage by letter to the very attractive golden-haired girl, a FANY and the belle-of-the-ball, whom he had got to know so well in Mombasa? He probably only wanted an audience. There was not much that I, in my inexperience, could contribute in advice to such a worldly personality.

Sometimes later, he showed me the "Dear John" letter in reply to his. This is Jack's name for a written brush off from a lady. In *Fortune* the recipient of one of these sad missives would often pin it on the notice board. A kind of public mourning band, it informed of a tragedy to be respected or alternatively a comedy to be made fun of, depending on the characters involved and length of time away from home.

There seemed to be little point of contact between the C.O. and his new First Lieutenant. Past fairly open disloyalty must have been somewhat inhibiting in the new relationship, which required regular communication. Not much changed otherwise, except that we were now one officer short for watchkeeping and extraneous duties. A Joker had also joined the pack in the shape of a small, dusky, over-confident midshipman, Royal Indian Navy, called Rao, who could not possibly have been intended as a replacement for a lieutenant.

Merchant ships continued to be sunk in the southern Indian Ocean. *Resolution* was torpedoed, but not sunk, by a Japanese submarine in Diego Suarez. We believed that there were one or two German U-boats supported by a supply ship operating around the area, but there was no useful Intelli-

gence. Unescorted ships were sitting ducks, their sailings reported by Nazi sympathisers, endemic in all South African ports. *Fortune* was now deployed as a regular single ship escort for small, often one ship, convoys between Durban and Capetown, with Simonstown as her base. Among these charges were the damaged *Resolution* and troopship *Orestes*, together with a number of merchant ships, whose cargo we would know nothing of unless they were sunk, when they literally spilled the beans.

This sounds a quiet number, which it certainly was compared with fighting Atlantic convoys through to Liverpool, Malta or Murmansk. But it was not a sinecure. Doenitz in his memoirs says, "The operation off Capetown was a complete success. In October we sank in this area twenty-seven ships, 161, 121 tons, many of which were loaded with important military cargoes . . . and valuable troopships." It became even less of a holiday, when Philip Archer-Shee went sick without warning and into hospital ashore. I wondered, unsympathetically, whether he might not be suffering from what in today's medical jargon is described as post-traumatic stress disorder.

Honk speaking: "Oh, Pilot, you are to be the First Lieutenant while Archer-Shee is in hospital," he announced with his customary abrupt delivery.

This took me by surprise. I thought for a moment, then said, "But, Sir, Lieutenant Mathews is years senior to me."

In the Royal Navy it was correct and normal for the next executive officer in Navy List order, whether R.N., R.N.R. or R.N.V.R., to step up one in an event of this kind. Or at least this is what I thought. Also I felt that I was being put in a position that was bound to offend Mathews, who apart from being senior was also much older. He might also be touchy on account of my straight stripes as a career officer.

"Pilot, you are now First Lieutenant. His mind was evidently made up.

"Aye, aye, sir," was all I could offer, meanwhile guiltily feeling secret pride that Roddy Macdonald should be elevated to "Jimmy" (first lieutenant of a fleet destroyer) when only twenty-one, albeit temporarily. Any possible satisfaction was more than tempered by an awareness of my total ignorance of how to set about the job. I suspected – in the event correctly – that no practical advice was likely to be on offer from my Captain. Then, thinking fast, I asked to whom he would like me to turn over the duties of navigation, signals and torpedo control. Presumably, I thought, this would be to Mathews, particularly navigation with its time conflicting requirements.

He gave me an odd look. "That's all right," he replied "you can go on with all your own jobs, Pilot."

He then turned on his heel and disappeared. He had a disconcerting habit of popping up and then vanishing as if through a trap door like a stage magician, to bring discussion to a close.

I went anxiously down to the ship's office, where I found Porny Mathews awash in an ocean of newly received official correspondence (war stops this not), and broke the unwelcome news to him as tactfully as possible. I added for good measure that, if he intended to protest, as he had every right to, he had better get cracking before Honk made some sort of public announcement.

Porny slit open a large buff envelope and spilled its unattractive contents onto the already heaped up desk. He leaned back, looked up at me and smiled with genuine amusement. "Congratulations, Pilot. You are very welcome, and the best of British luck. Have you heard the one about the village virgin and the vaulting vicar in the graveyard?" The question was evidently rhetorical and the anecdote often repeated and not worth repetition.

For the second time in rapid succession I was taken aback. The captain bullied him, I knew, and they despised each other. Anyway, this part of the day's manoeuvres had turned out to be not as tricky as I had expected. Porny Mathews was evidently unconcerned, or if he was he disguised it well. He seemed in no way put out by what amounted to an insulting, and tactlessly communicated, public supercession. Like Stripey, Porny was a philosopher.

Honk made no announcement. It occurred to me then that it was odd that, unlike other captains, he never once addressed the ship's company assembled together, an occasion for which lower deck would be cleared. Perhaps it was just as well as he would have made a hash of it. They only knew about the unorthodox decision – most of them anyway would not have cared one way or the other – by the newly elevated young officer's absurd double act on the bridge when shortly afterwards *Fortune* cast off and sailed from Simonstown bound for Durban

Me, speaking fast: "Ship secured for sea, sir. Ready to go to Defence Stations. Compass one degree high. Rung on. 100 revolutions. No tide. Wind on port bow. Let got aft. Let go head rope. Hold spring. Slow ahead port. Both engines half astern. Three short blasts. Stow away wires and fenders. Secure for rough weather with life lines. Buffer, who the hell is that showing a light by the vegetable locker? Clobber him, if you can. Secure anchors and cables. Hands to Action Stations, priority anti-submarine. Rendezvous convoy in half an hour. Canteen committee meeting postponed till tomorrow" – and even more of this absurd, but required, rigmarole. It involved jumping like a kangaroo from compass to bridge wing and back, hurdling telephone cables and other maritime equipment in the process. It certainly lacked dignity.

A trick cyclist riding two bicycles will injure only himself, should he fall off. In my situation, it seemed to me, I was wobbling between several handlebars, while simultaneously trying to hang wall paper. There seemed to be an infinite capacity to damage both the ship and the people in her. A temporary loan of a junior officer from C. in C. South Atlantic's shore staff could have been asked for in the circumstances, but for some inexplicable reason Honk would not ask. Perhaps he was worried about a spy in the camp.

Punctiliously he called me "Pilot" when I was navigating, and "Number One" when I was dealing with him on executive matters. I think he found it convenient to see me as two different officers. I fell in with this, and rapidly developed a split personality, using whichever I thought appropriate at the time. This dotty game, because it was vaguely entertaining, was useful to maintain some contact with reality. Sometimes I hammed (and egged) it up, which was not strictly proper, but fun. I certainly debated heatedly with myself when there was a conflict in ship priorities.

There followed several weeks when time failed to accommodate all these activities equally. But any lingering anxiety that I may have felt about discipline evaporated. The daily routine and so on had been well framed by Michael Morris. Change was not necessary. When called to do extra work at unpopular times, it was done well and cheerfully. I assumed that Jack, who likes underdogs, if he thought at all about it, felt sorry for me, and with good reason. In any case, I was to a point sorry for him too. I had in school holidays between the ages of nine and fifteen worked and fed with the labourers on a Scottish lowland farm and lived with the working family on a West Highland croft. The farm employees, who would not have recognised leadership had it been offered, were much less educated than Jack or the crofter, but this had given me some insight into the adversarial attitude of the British working man towards authority – apart from being able to hand milk three cows, and ride a Clydesdale carthorse bare back. Jimmy Green, the farm boy, used to write to me painfully and apparently with both hands when I went back to school. Also like all naval cadets of that time, I had in the training cruiser worked as a "mate" for a variety of sailor "tradesmen", carrying a tool bag and incidentally thereby learning the art of skiving.

As well as taking sights and establishing the ship's position at dawn, noon, dusk and other times, and by coastal pilotage, I kept the morning watch (0400 to 0800) on the bridge and often another. I took charge of the employment of the seamen, their weapon training, such as it was, and efficiency, their discipline and so on. As some activities were related to ship's daily administrative routine, such as the times the hands started work, and others were dictated by the movement of the ship, and heavenly bodies such as the sun, the stars and the moon, it was too easy to be in the wrong place or obeying the priority but one you last thought of. "Stripey" was overheard to compare my peripatetic movements to the buzzing of a "blue-arsed fly". Meanwhile, Honk visited the bridge at dusk and first light, otherwise remaining in his sea cabin.[1]

Then there were the formal occasions when sailors lined up with caps on, at the Captain's Table to "request" something, such as promotion, pay, and diverse administrative matters. Alternatively with cap off, they were there to be tried for doing something not cared for by the Naval Discipline Act, usually some minor misdemeanour. I was also responsible for victualling, which really did alarm me – particularly the accounting. All this went on while the ship was acting as Senior Officer of Escort of a convoy, where I was involved in responsibility for navigation and signals and the Asdic (Sonar) contact immediately interrupted everything. It occurred to me that if our head man accidentally fell overboard, or was pushed, I would qualify to be comprehensively the "Mate of *The Nancy Brig*".

I skimped, did nothing well and broke lots of regulations, such as employing the yeoman of signals to decrypt "officer only" signals. I delegated the victualling completely to a petty officer, fudging musters and asking Fred, the Gunner, to pretend he was checking up on my behalf. I promoted the Gunner's Mate, another petty officer, to Gun Director Controller in case we came across the *Hipper*. One afternoon at sea the doctor added to my Gilbertian status by asking me to assist with an intravenous anaesthetic that he wanted to administer in connection with minor surgery on a sailor, the ship rolling its guts out, mine too.

The too-clever-by-half Indian midshipman filled in spare time with tricky questions on theoretical navigation, which he knew that I could not answer without reference to a book – the answers to which, I suspected, he himself knew perfectly well. I reminded him unfairly that in the Navy a midshipman is the lowest form of life, even if his name might be Mountbatten or Prince Philip. His journal, which it was my unfortunate duty to inspect, did not disguise his hatred of the Empire and of British rule in India.

Meanwhile, except at the institutional events of Captain's Requestmen and Defaulters, already mentioned, I saw little more of the C.O. than I had

before. One possible advantage of his veneration for literal application o the King's Regulation was that he stuck "regardless" to the recommende scale for punishment. Mitigation, when advocated, seemed less accept able than piling on "aggravation". There was little to discuss unless it wa the sort of case where I had to avoid a giggle – for instance Jack, promi nently tattooed with "Death before Dishonour", relating an imaginativ tale to explain his lack of punctuality on returning from a binge in Durba or Capetown. It was necessary sometimes to fiddle charges down to th sort of level, that the First Lieutenant was allowed by the regulation to deal with, to avoid "flogging" a willing horse. As president of th Wardroom mess, although the most junior commissioned officer,[2] I was apart from the midshipman, the youngest member of it. If Honk was awar of all this, he gave no indication whatsoever. My impatience must hav been irritating to my elders, but they were remarkably tolerant. The docto did remind me once that, with a university degree, he was a superio being.

On 21 June when screening *Resolution* from Durban to Capetown, w were diverted to a U-boat contact about 160 miles east of Port Elizabeth This turned into a sadly customary search for lifeboats. U.S.V. *Pierc Butler* was the latest victim of the idiotic practice of sailing slow mer chantmen unescorted, for which the U.S.A. paid so much in tonnage an casualties.[3] There was no difficulty in locating the boats. Her crew o about sixty gratefully scrambled up the rope ladders and nets, encourage not to waste time in case *Fortune* attracted a torpedo. In this event the would be back, poor fellows, where they had come from. The boats wer sunk by gunfire – useful Rapid Open Fire practice.

There was a surprisingly large number of Chinese deck hands in the crew, understandably highly agitated and orientally nervous. They refused to leave the upper deck till the ship was safely alongside in Durban. There, as soon as the brow bridged the gap, they rushed ashore like frenzied lemmings, pushing Gilbert, Sullivan, Uncle Tom Cobley and all out of the way. The *Pierce Butler*'s Chief Officer, when leaving, remarked to the doctor that he was surprised that *Fortune*'s First Lieutenant devoted so little of his time to "chatting up" the passengers. I could have cheerfully slaughtered him.

Chapter 21

The Grudge Fight

Strange! that such high dispute shou'd be
Twixt Tweedledum and Tweedledee.
John Byrom 1692

Thought paralyses action.
Jean Cocteau

One day, while I was acting as First Lieutenant, *Fortune*, having brought in the north-bound convoy and the only warship there, was berthed alongside in the unsalubrious commercial port of Durban harbour. On a previous occasion, she had been berthed on a cattleship with fly blown sides streaming in ordure.[1] The Coxswain approached in the special manner that he used when he wanted to sell an idea, but was not too sure how it would be received.

"Them cock sparrah's in the upper seaman's messdeck are at it again. I would mess-change one or other, but no killick (leading hand) wants either of 'em." I knew that these two had fallen out – "got on each other's tits" – early on. Surprising as it may seem, when so many young men were required to live hugger mugger in a small mobile tin box, this type of personality clash did not often happen. Give and take was the accepted order with Jack.

"It's not as if it was about a woman or a football team. Just no reason. They don't think," he went on.

"Well, Coxswain, what do you suggest?" I asked.

"You know, a Grudge Fight would do the trick. I wasn't sure you would like the idea, being sort of unusual, but I think it would work. Anyway, they are both about the same size," he added hopefully, "though nowhere

near the same shape. It should be a fair go and they can let off steam in public."

I had vaguely heard of such an event. It figured somewhere in naval mythology, but did not appear within the pages of either K.R. & A.I. or the Physical Training Manual. Unencumbered as I was by experience, and with no wise shoulder to lean on, it seemed worth a try. I reassured myself that the proceedings could presumably be stopped if they got out of hand.

"All right, let's get on with it. How soon can you set it up?"

"It's now seven bells. Hands go to dinner in half an hour. They'll have had their tot (rum ration), so we can kick off at about 1230. It's a Make and Mend (half holiday). With any luck there won't be too many spectators. They'll be getting their heads down, as we have to slip after supper."

We were scheduled to take a convoy to the Cape.

"Right, go ahead," I replied, outwardly full of confidence; but, somewhere within, a smaller, slightly anxious self peered out, wondering what would happen next. "Make it look as 'pusser' (overtly legal) as possible."

I did not have long to wait. As if by magic, within forty minutes, a boxing ring had been rigged with ropes running from the torpedo tubes amidships, and out to the guard rails on the port side. Because of the limitations of a destroyer's narrow beam, the result was a rectangle. Coloured signal bunting decorated the corners and ammunition boxes served as stools. The iron deck had been covered by collision mats and canvas.

At precisely 1230 the Seconds, Stripey and Corky, exhibiting their qualifications, the former his broken nose and the latter a cauliflower ear, inspected the arrangements and shook hands with the referee. This role was filled by the Gunner's Mate, who was sporting a dilapidated top hot on which REF was painted in white, presumably as badge of office. A pause then ensued, attributed correctly to a disappointing lack of enthusiasm being displayed by the chief players.

Meanwhile, it became apparent that the Coxswain had underestimated Jack's interest. No public announcement had been made, yet the bush telegraph had created a larger muster than an organised Clear Lower Deck. Even the Engineroom Artificers were present in force. Messdeck stools, damage control shores and all sorts of boxes, and above these the torpedo walkway and search light platform, had become crowded grandstands. A "Squeejee" band consisting of two mouth organs, a jew's harp and the portable fog horn, a sort of overgrown bellows which grunted when squeezed, provided musical accompaniment. The flag deck for no known reason hoisted the church pendant, which hung limply up and down as there was no wind. It was beginning to resemble a peacetime regatta without boats.

A small procession eventually emerged from forward. First the Coxswain, representing Law and Order, followed by the contestants dressed in regulation shorts, singlets and gym shoes; then the Leading Hand of their mess with two sets of boxing gloves; and bringing up the rear the Sick Berth Attendant carrying a bag significantly marked with a large Red Cross. The doctor was ashore, having unselfishly given up his make-and-end to inspect the quality of nurses in a nearby hospital. By this time I suspected that both belligerents would have given a lot to escape what they had come to realise would be a public ordeal. Neither, unusually for them, looked the least bit "stroppy".

While gloves were laced up, the audience offered advice. Sides were taken more or less indiscriminately. Terrible Petty Officer Jacko, wearing a brown billycock hat, ran a book on the outcome, recording the odds with coloured chalk on a blackboard secured to the vegetable locker abreast the forward funnel. A handful of sawdust and the scent of resin and cigar smoke added atmosphere.

"By kind permission of the First Lieutenant," the referee announced, thus tactfully reminding me of my personal responsibility in the event of something going wrong, "this contest under the Marquis of Queensbury rules has been arranged to sort out the grudge existing between – in the blue corner, George the Gorilla, and in the red corner, Gentleman Jim – and may the best man win."

The audience roared. Interest became apparent on the jetty above. Here the spectators looked rather like Zulus dressed up as dockyard riggers, which is precisely what they were.

"Seconds out of the ring". The Timekeeper, Leading Supply Assistant Galloway, without removing his cigar and using a wheel spanner, struck the 4.7-inch calibre empty brass cordite cylinder, suspended on a bowline from the guardrail. Stripey and Corky each gave his own pugilist an encouraging shove off between the shoulder blades towards the centre of the ring where they could not avoid shaking hands, perhaps for the first time ever.

The contestants, conscious of all eyes upon them, now adopted the postures in which they had been coached by their Seconds. George, a short thick-set hirsute youth, crouched with his head down, chin tucked into chest and gloves in front of face. In profile he resembled a question mark. Someone shouted, "Come on, the Gorilla." Jim, by contrast stood bolt upright much in the classical style of an eighteenth-century prize fighter. One glove was extended at arm's length as far as it would go. The other waved about in front of his chest. "Ten to one on the Gent," sang out the billy cock hat. "Come on the Gorilla, sock 'im one!" "Get stuck in!" encouraged the audience. "Sippers for a knockout."

Meanwhile, the reluctant pair perambulated clockwise, facing each other with their respective sterns as close to the ropes as they could manage, earning an encouraging push from their corners as the opportunity arose. One minute had now passed without a blow being landed, or for that matter attempted.

"Windy! The sun's burning yer eyes out," and various uncomplimentary remarks on character and personal appearance were offered by spectators. Stimulated by a particularly wounding and unrepeatable insult, the Gorilla rushed forward and swung a prodigious right hook. Had this connected it would have settled the argument once and for all. Unfortunately, or perhaps fortunately, the Gorilla's eyes were closed in sheer terror – shades of my school boxing experience. His wildly circling glove missed the Gent's nose by six inches. Driven by its own volition, it carried on with its owner, so that he performed a *pas de chat*, which would have passed muster with the Ballet Russe. Tottering dizzily into a corner, he was returned to the middle by a quick push.

Encouraged by his opponent's ineptitude and a chorus of derision from the audience, the Gent advanced circumspectly with his left arm fully extended to ensure that the Gorilla remained at a respectable distance. From this strategic position he embarked without preliminaries on a stupendous upper cut. This had little chance of reaching the Gorilla's chin simply because it was still over an arm's length away. The blow nevertheless whistled upwards with considerable velocity, so that its architect, who was leaning cautiously away from his opponent at an angle of ten degrees, fell onto his back with a tremendous thump. A clang signalled the end of round one.

The fact that neither had so far hit the other, and that this was the object of the exercise, was drawn eloquently to their attention in sea-faring language. Insults rained down from every direction, not least from our Impi on the dockside. Colourful doubts were expressed by Jack on the parentage of the participants and their value to a warship, whose purpose was after all to "fuckin' fight". This last was, of course, a gross slander because everyone knew that neither young man had ever shown himself to be other than brave under enemy fire.

Both Seconds put on a big act. The Gorilla had a gallon of cold water poured down inside his shorts by Stripey. The Gent's stomach was alternately pummelled and massaged by Corky's horny hands. Noses were vigorously fan-flicked with Admiralty pattern towels. The brass cylinder clanged for the second round. Ammo' boxes were yanked out and opponents once again encouraged to wallop each other. Terrible Petty officer Jacko now accepted side bets on which of the warriors would connect first.

At this moment a *"deus ex machina"* in the shape of the harbour oil fuel lighter, whose approach the Quartermaster had failed to detect – owing to understandable distraction of his attention towards the dramatic events taking place inboard – berthed alongside with an almighty bang. The impact caused *Fortune* to lurch to port, and then sharply back to starboard as she rebounded off the dock wall fenders.

The effect of such sudden and unexpected instability on our humiliated heroes was dramatic. The crouching Gorilla, propelled precipitately, head-butted his opponent in the stomach. The Gent, completely winded and gasping for breath in distress, doubled up, raising his knees violently upwards under the Gorilla's chin and knocked him out. A genuine war dance could be seen and heard up above on the dock wall. Two horizontal

champs were formally counted out by the Gunner's Mate, who announced to a chorus of "Stone the crows, corfuck!" and good-natured laughter that the contest was judged a fair old draw. Then in the same breath, "Starboard Watch muster amidships. Stow away gear. Secure for sea – storm warning forecast."

"That'll fix 'em," said the Coxswain with quiet satisfaction, and he was right.

Chapter 22

Round the Bend

And a good south wind sprung up behind;
The albatross did follow,
And every day, for food or play,
Came to the mariners hollo!
"The Ancient Mariner"

Unlike Moby Dick and other well-known maritime sagas, there is no climax, no bang, to round off this story. Our "figurehead" kept well below the parapet, the doorstep of his cabin, an unusual posture for someone commanding one of His Majesty's ships in war. The ship with her people got on somehow with her business without any noticeable contribution from her C.O. Focus of operations had transferred to the Cape of Good Hope. We would have undoubtedly benefited from a battle in defence of a convoy. Perhaps it was as well that there was no battle, because we were

virtually a ship Not under Command. Anyway, Jack was already in his favourite pub somewhere north of Ushant. His philosophy could be summed up as "Heads down; count the days; don't push your luck" – and all this without any hint of a date for return to the U.K. or for paying off.

Work was willingly done and behaviour when ashore was civilised in spite of the temptation to let the end go. Jack's imagination had focussed on a fantastic welcome home, in which active sex figured as of more than passing interest. It was impossible now to differentiate between the regular and the Hostilities Only sailor, so much had one stamped his character and way of life on the other. Being locked up together in a small mobile tin box afloat on salt water had something to do with a natural conformity in behaviour, language and attitude.

But the enemy, operating probably two U-boats and up to three raiders with supply ships, disguised as merchantmen, in the South Atlantic and Southern Indian Ocean, called the tune with economy and minimum force. There was neither air support nor reconnaissance available to conduct a search or to strike what was found. An unfair jest was current: Q. Why are the South African Air Force called Penguins? A. One in a thousand flies. Thus December found *Fortune* searching the Roaring Forties about 200 miles south of the Cape for survivors of the (yet again) unescorted, and torpedoed, cargo vessel *Jeremiah Wadsworth.*

Carried away by unthinking and immature enthusiasm, in my capacity as acting first lieutenant I persuaded Honk, when we found the remains of the cargo, an acre of floating heavy duty lorry tyres originally bound for Australia, to salvage some because of its obvious value to the war effort. Covered in sticky black oil fuel, it was hell to embark. The sailors justifi-

ably grumbled, but did their best, particularly when I, disingenuously, put it about that there might be salvage money in the offing. For some strange reason, it was only later that it sunk in that the risk of attracting a torpedo from a lurking U-boat made this an unprofitable exchange. Landed on the jetty at Capetown, our tyre collection proved of so little interest to anyone that it was still there when we finally left the area. (In the U.K. £500 1942 value or three years imprisonment was the penalty for wasting rubber of any sort.)[1] Four fruitless days were spent on the search for survivors in the Roaring Forties.[2] A single wandering albatross kept us company in this watery waste. It was our constant companion. Everyone was relieved that the captain's .22 rifle had been landed for compulsory refit.

The tall cheerful figure of Philip Archer-Shee was on the jetty when we returned. He was in good heart and I was relieved to be able to concentrate on my own job at a less rip-roaring pace. Meanwhile, at each short visit between convoys our dusky Indian midshipman was ejected without ceremony from Capetown cinemas[3] because of his colour. It was disgraceful, but there was nothing we could do about it. Dumpy little Rao was determined and courageous. The more often he was thrown out, the more often he went back to be thrown out again. He was a high caste Brahmin, and both cocky and pompous – not a bit like the very laid-back Royal Indian Navy cadets who had been my mess mates in the Training Cruiser.[4] It would have been too much to expect him to measure his treatment by South Africans against his own of inferior castes at home; not that anyone would have been tactless enough to suggest it. This was such a bad appointment for diplomatic reasons, that he was transferred to a ship going elsewhere. How this came about was a mystery, as Honk appeared to take little interest. Perhaps Porny forged his Captain's signature on a letter to C. in C. South Atlantic with a strong recommendation for re-appointment to a big ship.

Chapter 23

Sippers

And the pencil of the Holy
Ghost hath laboured more
in describing the afflictions of
Job than the felicities of Solomon.
Bacon

If the ship enjoyed two days in harbour,[1] she attracted all sorts of extraneous duties. *Fortune* from C. in C. South Atlantic: "Provide ceremonial funeral party for burial of Bill Bloggs, Ordinary Seaman, late of *Dandelion* (Corvette).[2] Apart from the C.O., I was the only commissioned officer on board with any knowledge of this particular drill, which had ludicrously (or was it practical in a macabre sort of way?) absorbed as much time and effort during sublieutenant's courses as anti-submarine warfare. The unfortunate Bloggs was a casualty of a liberal offering of rum (illegal sippers) from his shipmates on his twenty-first birthday, offers probably impossible to refuse. The consequence was that he choked to death in his hammock. Meanwhile, his ship with his messmates were again at sea on escort duty in the Atlantic.

So there we all were in white Number One uniform together with the hearse at the cemetery gates; the instant funeral party, "cheerful but subdued" as laid down in the manual, with Lee Enfield rifles reversed; the gunner's mate with his cutlass and me with my sword – but no sign of chaplain. Nobody represented the C.O. of *Dandelion*, although I felt sure that it was our Captain's duty to do so. Time passed. Remembering that the manual, and parade ground instructors, placed great emphasis on punctuality (the Creator was involved) for funerals, I set the cortege going at a slow but dignified pace. Behind the oleanders that flowered down the

side of the avenue, I glimpsed a vision in white. It flapped wildly by and met us next to the grave with a broadside of unchristian recrimination. The padre was of course right, even though he was late and rather silly. It was I who had "warmed the bell (started early)". The funeral party enjoyed the interesting, and to them entertaining, diversion. It needed to, since poor Bloggs had no mourners, no friends, no mum or dad to see him off; not even a photographer to record the occasion. In a way he might have been any of us and we knew it.

* * *

Able Seaman Fitzgerald – he who had fired the Snow Flake rocket off Gibraltar and shot down the Italian torpedo bomber – was a good-looking sailor, strong and always exceptionally well turned out for a run ashore. In peacetime he was employed by a well-known soft drink company.[3] He returned from visiting its local factory carrying a small box containing

their products, which he had been given by his hosts as a present. It was so labelled. The ship was berthed at Capetown. Unlike Simonstown, a friendly little naval dockyard, the gates were manned by South African military-style police, some of whom were tough and appeared to have pro-Nazi tendencies. One of these questioned Fitzgerald aggressively about the contents of the box. Not satisfied with an entirely sober explanation, he demanded brusquely that it should be opened. Fitzgerald unwisely refused. What is called an altercation followed, culminating in the policeman receiving a "fourpenny one" and Fitzgerald being locked up.

Philip Archer-Shee took me with him to Capetown, when he attended the court at which Fitzgerald appeared before a single magistrate. Being a Reserve officer, it was Philip's first experience representing Jack in trouble, but it was also mine. We found our man in a smelly communal lock-up together with riff-raff picked up in the city the night before, mainly Cape Coloured prostitutes and alcoholic vagrants. In spite of these unpleasant conditions, he looked immaculate, which is more than can be said of the tough young policeman, who sported a black eye. Evidence was heard entirely in Africaans. It was a toss up whether to mention Fitzgerald's personal success in action in the Mediterranean, because how it was received depended on where our magistrate's wartime sympathies lay. We closed our eyes, trusting to fortune, gambled and got it right. Able Seaman Fitzgerald was "bound over" – in the middle of a world war – "to keep the peace".

Chapter 24

Distance Lends Enchantment

The Captain was a duck with a packet on his back;
And when the ship got under way
The Captain said, Quack, Quack!

Then right at the end of January 1943, when cafard (Foreign Legion style) through lack of action was beginning to set in, *Fortune* was ordered, apparently out of the blue, to return home to refit. It had been a

well-concealed secret. Jack new already because these things cannot be kept from him. We were to form part of a powerful escort for fast Convoy C.F. 11 bound via Freetown for Liverpool. This included my old ship *Valiant*[1] and the big liners *Britannic* and *Orion*, both employed as troop ships.

Records show that seventy-three ships (429,891 tons of shipping) were sunk, mainly by U-boats, in the North Atlantic during February. The ships in our fast convoy were capable of twenty knots. The escort was a strong one and composed of fleet destroyers. U-boats had so many softer targets to go for. Luckily the German Airforce Fuhrer, Hermann Goering,[2] did not understand the significance of the Atlantic battle and allotted it low priority for reconnaissance or anything else. So the passage home, including a brief stop at Freetown, was without operational incident. A signal to *Fortune* from the screen commander – "Distance lends enchantment" – was earned on an occasion when, to get a closer look at the attractive girls lining the troop ship's guard rails, one of whom I had got to know well in the Cape, *Fortune* deviated from the most direct route through the convoy when ordered to change station on the screen. This elegant reproof was the most cheerful signal that *Fortune* had ever received in the whole commission for station-keeping or anything else.

Off the Scillies *Fortune*, to Jack's delight, was diverted by her Admiralty fairy godmother up Channel to London to refit in the Isle of Dogs, not too far from where most of the ship's company came from. I knew this to be a desolate area of dockland lying within a loop of the Thames and pitted with bomb craters. My twenty-second birthday on 25th February

went uncelebrated like my twenty-first, but this time cheerfully butting through the English Channel past struggling mine sweepers rather than steaming lugubriously on top of the Arabian sea.

I insisted, and Honk accepted, that no Thames river pilot was needed and enjoyed steering the ship past innumerable mudbanks, wrecks, minefields and bomb-damaged buildings. Nothing any longer was navigationally difficult. I had grown up. Honk's father, a retired Army colonel, genial and appropriately clad in felt hat and British Warm, joined by boat somewhere to seaward of Greenwich.

Fortune berthed at dusk within the purlieus of The London Graving Docks Company, and rang off engines for the last time just as the evening's first air raid syrens wailed. The scenery resembled a painting of the Battle of the Somme, except that jagged vertical steel girders represented tree trunks, sharply black against the last glimmer of winter light. Honk, with evident surprise, said, "You Know, Pilot, my father said that he was impressed by the way you brought the ship up the Thames." I was touched by this unexpected compliment, particularly as none of the pilotage had been difficult. Afterwards I realised that this

was the first "well done", albeit secondhand, that I could remember Honk handing out to anyone since *Fortune* left Chatham sixteen months before. I personally did not deserve it. *Fortune*'s people certainly did.

My last small service on Honk's behalf was to turn a blind eye, in my capacity as Officer of the Day, when his duty free wine stores were disembarked. I supposed that, with so much destruction around, the Inland Revenue was unlikely to be concerned with a minor deficit. I was reminded of this in a letter forty years later from the Quartermaster, Hostilities only Able Seaman Butler, who was manning the gangway at the time. He wrote that I had given him a "strong telling off" for something he knew nothing about, though he suspected it was to do with the captain's steward and the captain's wines. Perhaps that is how I earned a friendly confidential report from Honk.

Chapter 25

Fortune's People

He asked the Duke "What is necessary in ruling a kingdom?"
The Duke replied; "Essere umano" – *"to be human."*
Civilisation, Kenneth Clark

Within days the good ship, that had been our home for so long, lay dishevelled, lifeless, silent and cold in dry dock.[1] After disembarking stores and ammunition, *Fortune*'s people, officers and ratings, were scattered throughout the Navy and around the world in different ships, never except by chance to meet again. Many would not survive the war. In happier ships "paying off" at the end of a commission is an emotional occasion. Jolly, sentimental, none too serious re-unions organised by Jack go some way to make up for this. Peering through the wrong end of a telescope – naval equivalent of rose-coloured spectacles – brings back memories of comradeship and a shared sense of purpose. Without glorifying war, many wartime sailors believe that these were their great days. But there is always the exception.

Jack

From *Fortune* Jack just pushed off rejoicing – always the optimist, confident that it never blows as hard twice running. Ten, even fourteen, exciting days of long leave lay ahead – perhaps longer, if "Draftie" mislaid an official number or two. He did not know – none of us knew – how long the war would last. It might go on for ever. To guarantee a dreamy home-coming, he had taken the precaution of bearing gifts, some with mythical aphrodisiac reputation, such as oranges, bananas, cigarettes, sugar, lipstick and silk stockings – the cherished cargo *Fortune* had recently butted up the Channel. How these heroes, bronzed from a pack-

aged cruise on full, though admittedly modest, pay recently under the Southern Cross, were received by their nearest and dearest, accustomed to dank air raid shelters and routine nightly blitz,[2] will never be known. One hopes that it was up to expectation.

Armed with a stem of bananas – creating a sensation with such an unbelievable phenomenon down the Old Kent Road – and the last to go over the ship's side, Stripey, whose wife was reputed to bark like a Regulating Petty Officer, handed the Coxswain a pre-paid telegram addressed to himself to be despatched after forty-eight hours. The message read, "You are urgently required on board for duty. Leave cancelled. Signed Coxswain. H.M.S. *Fortune*."

The Officers

Surprising as it may seem, although no phalanx marched in closer step, *Fortune*'s officers wasted little time on fond farewell. After a celebration designed to absorb what was drinkable in the Wine Store, they were off dispersing with relief just like Jack. Within three or four weeks all of us were at sea again, but in other ships with other people and rather different commanding officers. Meanwhile the war went on and on. That we lost touch with each other in the circumstances is not surprising, but it was indeed a loss. At the time we had felt sure that somehow, somewhere, we would bump into each other again.

Thirty years or so later on a windy winter's day I was battling my way along the Thames Embankment near Cleopatra's Needle, when I saw a stalwart figure approaching, leaning into the stiff breeze, a red and blue scarf streaming pennant-like to leeward. The face was more florid, but the eyes as blue as ever. It was unmistakably Commander Michael Morris, Royal Navy, now long retired. "Good to see you," he bawled, making himself heard above the combined noise of traffic, wind and clanking chain cable along the water's edge – just as if we had accidentally met after a short voyage. Then, taking my arm, he steered me towards the ship *Wellington*, the Headquarters of the Honourable Company of Master Mariners, berthed alongside. There, over a glass of gin, we set the world to right – and remembered *Fortune*, her people and Honk. It was all so long ago that it might have been some strange dream, had it not been true. Michael and I remained in touch thereafter until he died – a very professional sea officer of the old school and a fine leader of men.

The Ship

H.M.S. *Fortune* herself, after a much needed refit and minor improvement to weapons and radar, was transferred to the rapidly expanding Royal Canadian Navy and renamed H.M.C.S. *Saskatchewan*. During the remainder of the war she fought in the Battle of the Atlantic, and successfully escorted a great many convoys and military formations involved in the invasion of Normandy. She finally paid off on 28th January 1946 at Sydney, Nova Scotia, and was subsequently broken up. She was thirteen years old – out of date when new – and by now a prematurely old lady. But she had paid for herself over and over again, and she had more than justified her name.

In the course of the war she had sunk two German U-boats and a Vichy French submarine.[3] She had helped to screen three or four fleets and escorted a massive tonnage of merchant shipping. She had earned her Battle Honours, *Atlantic*, *Norway*, *Malta Convoys*, several times over. She was a lucky ship, when one remembers that, not counting other classes of escort such as corvettes and frigates, 135 destroyers in the Royal Navy went to the bottom in World War II.

Captain

To command a destroyer for sixteen months in war and bring her home undamaged was no mean feat. As far as the world knew, he had done well. *Fortune* had not lost one ship in any of the many convoys where Honk had been the Escort Force Commander. His ship had performed satisfactorily under multiple air attack in Operation *Vigorous*. There was no record of anything out of place in discipline or administration, and no black marks for tactical, navigational or ship handling incidents. The last three achievements are more than could be said of Earl Mountbatten's performance in the destroyers that he commanded.

Our hero was of course known to be odd and a loner, but these are scarcely recognised blots on character. His ship had never spent long enough with any administrative authority for the regulations to trigger a routine confidential report on him. Experienced destroyer captains had become rare, like gold dust; and many, inevitably after several years of intense action, had come to the end of their tether. *Fortune*'s C.O. was undoubtedly experienced. So, in the summer of 1944 during the latter stages of the war, he was given command of a modern destroyer, relieving another Lt. Commander, worn out by horrific Russian convoys – for which incidentally the dreadful Stalin never thanked us. Admiralty wisdom may have appreciated that a figurehead was all that this war-weary ship needed. Then, out of the blue, Fortune's Wheel spun once more and Honk was awarded the Distinguished Service Cross. He was transformed – in media terms a "war hero". If not quite in a flash converted by fairy wand into a handsome prince, it was reported that he had become "almost human". "He was no worse," according to a junior R.N.V.R. officer in this last ship, "than any other R.N. captain. And," he added with some conviction, "I should know as my father was one."

Honk, who is now dead, had demonstrated in *Fortune* that whatever qualities a man may lack there is only one which in a commander is essential and that is humanity. The salutary effect of an award for distinguished service on someone, who had found it too difficult to hand out any acknowledgement to others, was remarkable. What a pity that this happy event did not precede his time in *Fortune*.

The discreditable incidents, described, were to put it mildly not normal, actually they were exceptional. But, having happened, there is little purpose to be gained in sweeping them under the carpet. It is better that knowing what can happen may help to prevent it happening again. The selection of Honk to command a destroyer did not arise just because it was "Buggins' turn", or as a result of blindfold selection by an uncaring system, but from the hard-pressed Navy List completely running out of Bugginses. This was due to the rapid expansion of the fleet, to casualties and to the extreme length of a rough old world war.

But the story does go some way to show what a run-of-the-mill, that is a standard, wartime ship's company of Jolly Jacks, when lead by loyal officers and senior rates, can achieve under unpromising and at times unsavoury conditions – circumstances that might well have floored a less resilient collection of humanity. The pathetic Honk, with so much professional training and experience under his belt, had been allocated a decision-making responsibility that he was by character and personality incapable of exercising, except perhaps as a figurehead. It was only many years later that I came to realise that he must have known this only too well himself. His inner turmoil during the incidents related here must have been painful, even excruciating.

Junior Lieutenant

When I came to the end of forty years rewarding, and frequently entertaining, occasionally even exciting, service in the Royal Navy, much of it at sea – riding a continuous learning curve, but never so steep or irregular as in *Fortune* – I was delighted to hear that a very senior officer had summed me up – "Roddy Macdonald. No brains. Lots of common sense." Had he known half the story of *Fortune* and her figurehead, he might have added "and very lucky too". After all, a lucky ship shares her luck with those that serve in her.

Battle of the Atlantic

A speech by Vice Admiral Sir Roderick Macdonald, K.B.E., at the Royal Naval Club, Hill Street, London, 17 May 1991.

Shortly before the war I joined, with my friend Terry Lewin, His Majesty's ship *Belfast* (then at Scapa Flow and not Tower Bridge) as a cadet earning four and sixpence a day. Ordered to deliver a frightfully urgent letter to another cruiser, I drove my picket boat flat out regardless through a thick fog to the jetty, wearing because of the conditions a cork life jacket – ran like a rigger along it in zero visibility – suddenly heard "'ooh-goes-there?"-"'Alt-or-I-fire" – and was simultaneously impaled by a fixed bayonet held, eyeball to eyeball by an anxious looking matelot in a tin hat. When I returned the severed remains of the regulation pusser's life jacket to the stores petty officer, he remarked gloomily, "this is the sort of thing that gets war a bad name." Incidentally it was only on a recommendation of the Royal Oak enquiry that individual life belts were issued to ships' companies.

Proud as I am to have been an occasional insignificant cog in this great battle, I have to admit that no Atlantic convoy, in which my ships sailed, was interfered with by U-boats – all arrived in a safe and more or less timely manner in spite of bombs, mines, E-boats and on one occasion shore batteries. (There were of course stimulating and less successful times elsewhere in other oceans.)

How cosy it would be to attribute this to escort efficiency. In fact it only goes to show the success of convoy, which among other things, empties the ocean of fortuitous targets, especially when routed on super intelligence.

A cruise down memory lane is awash with appalling weather, open bridges, freezing sea water on the wrong side of oilskins and seaboots, unlit ships obstinately zigging the wrong way, the world lurching apparently to its end and the unfortunate newly joined bridge lookout being sick to windward.

I have one or two appropriate anecdotes from my friends selected ruthlessly from many. Those present will, I am sure, cap them later. But first the serious stuff.

Convoy seems to have been the only important lesson derived from World War One. And it still makes sense, that is, provided there are any merchant ships left to convoy, or escorts and aircraft with which to escort them.

Mistakes and omissions

How was it that our distinguished predecessors were so unready for a U-boat offensive after only 20 years since the last one? For instance, there is no record of any exercise in the protection of a slow convoy against submarine or air attack between 1919 and 1939; there was unjustifiable reliance on a primitive underwater sound detection system even though U-boats had attacked on the surface at night in World War One; and escorts were designed for a second Jutland and not for anti-submarine work in the Atlantic.

Specialisation in anti-submarine warfare was thought of as second class, even non-U, compared to say gunnery, torpedoes and signals. Even after two years of war we R.N. sublieutenants on courses suffered more time on the parade ground than we spent in an anti-submarine trainer. There was zero priority for appropriate aircraft and weapons for Coastal Command and Fleet Air Arm. All these are undeniably professional cockups, not political ones.

War, they say, is generally won by the side that makes the least mistakes. So it was fortunate that we had valuable co-operation from Messrs Hitler, Goering and Grand Admiral Raeder.

These three succeeded in buggering up the only individual who could have won it for them, the U-boat C.-in-C., Doenitz. He ran his side of the Atlantic battles with a handful of temporarily shore drafted U-boat officers; Luftwaffe supremo Goering agreed with his U.K. 'oppos', such as 'bomber' Harris, on the insignificance of sea war.

It is absurd that this campaign should be called a battle. It must have been, to coin a phrase, the 'mother of all battles', since in the history of man no battle has lasted as long or been fought against such odds for the benefit of so many, or indeed by so many.

Oscars

I cannot list all the arms, services and people, whose contribution brought us victory. It would be like a show biz Hammy Award act. Also omissions will get me into trouble. For instance, there was Ultra's dominating contribution. Nevertheless I offer three Oscars:

One. Jolly Jack. Without the tremendous support and heart warming humour of the ships' companies, that manned an incredible assortment of old and unsuitable iron in appalling conditions, we would have been utterly lost.

Two. The Royal Canadian Navy, which overcame exceptional material and training deficiencies, and much stick from its American and British Allies. But by early 1943 half the escorts between New York and the U.K. were Canadians. By 1944 Canada was carrying the main burden of the mid-Atlantic war. A Canadian corvette, sharpened up by the R.N. Escort Commander for indifferent station keeping, replied: 'Submit not too bad for a chartered accountant.'

My final Oscar goes to Admiral Sir Max Horton, C.-in-C. Western Approaches. Doenitz's memoirs claim that Churchill personally selected Horton as his, Doenitz's, adversary-in-chief. All the more suprising that the victor was so minimally honoured and his name virtually forgotten. Oddly the fellow he defeated became the last Führer. 'The evil that men do lives after them, the good is oft interred with their bones.'

To these and so many others, we owe our freedom to say what we like, to refuse to pay our taxes, join C.N.D., and vote for politicians, who in their wisdom economise on defence and turn a blind eye to the destruction of the merchant navy – something which U-boats failed to do in two world wars. Of the 138 ships chartered for the Gulf War only three were British. Without command of the sea this deployment would have been impossible.

For the first two years of the war R.A.F. Coastal Command had not one aircraft capable of reaching mid Atlantic. Air Vice Marshal Ted Hawkins describes how, appropriately on Trafalgar Day 1941, two newly acquired Catalina flying boats took off from Lough Erne to investigate an Admiralty HF/DF radio intercept of a U-boat happily transitting surfaced in mid Atlantic towards a convoy. After nine hours' flying and 700 miles in foul weather and radio silence both aircraft sighted the U-boat – fortuitously at the same time – and attacked. The significance was the signal it gave to the enemy that the mid Atlantic gap was to be a gap no longer. But this was by no means to be a quick fix. Losses were huge.

In April and May 1943 came the turning point. New ships organised as support groups, more long range aircraft for coastal command and the arrival of the escort carrier. A combined effort: lessons had been learned the hard way. Dedicated training paid dividends.

Talking of training: last time I saw Monkey Stevenson, terror of Tobermory, he was pushing ninety. Before a naval dinner, armed with a hearing aid, a stick and umbrella he was doing his best to pinch the bottom of the girl who was hanging up his hat.

The first British manned escort carrier, *Archer*, described by David Corkhill, an embarked Swordfish observer, as not pretty but happy and efficient, was a converted merchantman with flight deck propped up on poles forward and unreliable engines. The Swordfish or 'Stringbag' she carried were by contrast utterly reliable, but somewhat slow. David recalls once being overtaken by a double decker bus.

After an uneventful westbound convoy *Archer*'s return trip included an attack by five U-boats on one forenoon; two were dealt with by Liberators and three by Swordfish. Sublieutenant Horrocks, R.N.V.R., on patrol in his Swordfish sighted U 572 and under cover of cloud managed to get within 300 yards before firing his rocket projectiles. One pierced the U-boat's hull. Unable to dive, it surfaced to fight it out. Horrocks called up one of *Archer*'s Grumman Martlet fighters, which machine gunned the U-boat, and it sank. This was the first ever rocket projectile fired operationally by the allies. Sadly gallant young Horrocks did not survive the war.

Vice Admiral Sir Peter, then Commander, Gretton was, like Captains Johnnie Walker and Donald MacIntyre, a most successful and dedicated escort group commander. Well known to be an arch-workaholic, when others went on leave he locked himself in an office at the base and devised new ways to sink U-boats. No one could understand how he managed to find time to grab himself one of the prettiest girls in Derry. He is not, I am sorry, well enough to supply an anecdote, but his message relayed by Wren, now Lady Gretton is: Churchill said, "The only thing that ever really frightened me during the war was the U-boat peril;" said Peter (and I know of no one who disagrees), "If we had lost the battle of the Atlantic, we would have lost the war."

At this point we should remember that in only the first twenty days of March 1943 more than half a million tons of shipping had been sunk in the Atlantic. This anecdote recalls both the chaos of battle and the results achieved by intensive training.

Captain, then Lieutenant, Ray Hart, commanding the elderly destroyer *Vidette*, describes how Peter's B7 group on the evening of 5 May 1943 was escorting west bound convoy ONS 5, a mixed bag of forty-two ships, accompanied by rescue vessels and two inadequate auxiliary tankers. It had already been at sea for nearly two weeks in atrocious weather, negotiating icefloes, speed sometimes down to zero. Part of the convoy was straggling. Two ships collided. Shortage of fuel had reduced the escort.

Alerted by a Bletchley Park Decrypt, Max Horton ordered the 3rd Support Group to join. So far nine merchant ships had been sunk and a number of attacks by surfaced U-boats had been fought off the previous night.

Doenitz now sent an exhortation to all U-boats operating around ONS 5. "Immediately after onset of night the drum roll is to begin. Make haste. As there are forty of you, there will be nothing of the convoy left. The battle cannot last long as the sea space left is short. Use every chance to the full with all your might."

When night fell the corvette *Loosestrife* (the corvettes present were all commanded by Reserve Officers), detected a U-boat on radar. She gave chase, opened fire, forced it to dive and then depth charged it. Detecting another on the surface she closed at speed, intending to ram. The U-boat fired two torpedoes, which missed, then dived and was promptly depth charged and sunk.

On the other side of the convoy the frigate *Tay*, (Lieut. Cdr Sherwood, R.N.R.), was now Acting Group Commander, because Peter Gretton's *Duncan* had to withdraw to fuel and the weather, to Peter's chagrin, made it impossible for him to change ships. U-boat after U-boat kept appearing and doing their best to sink the two other corvettes, *Sunflower* and *Snowflake*. Torpedoes were everywhere. *Snowflake* by this time had only two depth charges left. When the U-boat dived she attacked it twice, using one each time.

The destroyer *Oribi* got a radar contact on a U-boat, which emerged out of the fog on a collision course. She rammed it abaft the conning tower. The U-boat unable to dive, manned its gun but ran straight into the arms of *Snowflake*, who shot her up, causing the crew to bale out and scuttle. *Sunflower* the rammed and ran right over another U-boat.

Meanwhile *Vidette* had been fully engaged against six U-boats. With so many U-boats waiting to find a gap in the screen it was only possible for the escorts to counter attack each contact with depth charges, then get back into station. This Ray did with the first five. The sixth he caught at shallow depth, when *Vidette* was running back towards the convoy, and sank it with Hedgehog ahead-thrown bombs.

In just this one night twenty-five attacks had been dealt with without loss of a ship against what had been the biggest concentration of U-boats in the war. Tragically overall thirteen merchant ships were lost. But ten U-boats had been sunk and five severely damaged, including those intercepted by two R.C.A.F. Catalinas, an R.A.F. Liberator and a U.S.A.F. Fortress. No Escort was lost.

Shortly after this Doenitz, recognising defeat, withdrew most of his boats from the Atlantic. The way was now ready for the invasion of Europe.

Had this been a land battle, or a sea fight of old, its name would be in the history books, like Salamis or Trafalgar. This was no skirmish. The fight to defend convoy ONS 5 was of more significance than Alamein.

Before my next story I must remind you that the death rate in our merchant navy was higher than in any of the other forces. Freedom does not come cheap.

The Red Duster story comes from Captain Arthur Blackham. He is writing a book that tells it. He recalls, without much affection, an eccentric bible-punching Welsh master, who owing to being a pacifist tried to stop him opening fire at a Heinkel that was machine gunning the ship.

"The battle of the Atlantic," Arthur says, "was a boring business for most of the time". An understatement, you will appreciate, from one for whom the life boat jump was no novelty. "Between 1940 and 1944 many voyages passed without incident. When something happened," he continued. "it happened very quickly. With total radio silence and no lights at night, occasionally escort vessels would steam madly round and round perhaps dropping depth charges, but they never told us why.

"Our main problems were of our own making. The *Thistleford*, a coal-burning steamer, could make eight and a half knots in smooth water with a good head of steam. In heavy weather and with an assortment of Liverpool stokers she was lucky to make eight. On one convoy we were outside column leader, but had trouble in maintaining station. Towards dusk we started falling back in spite of dire threats for more revolutions. Eventually the two ships astern overtook us and we became third in the column.

"We had barely settled down at number three when a torpedo hit the column leader and another hit the second ship. Depth charges started going off. What we did know was that our 'Scouse'stokers never stopped reminding us of what would have been the result, if they had had a full head of steam at the time." Arthur comments, "nowadays we would be counselled about stress problems, but fortunately that lot were all doing war jobs." It seems to me the shorter the war, the more the counselling.

When after the war was over I visited the German port of Emden in my first command, a Castle class corvette, we invited the naval club on board, mainly weathered ex U-boat officers. The group gathered round the ahead-throwing mortar and took of their hats. "This", they said, "is the thing that beat us."

Kenneth Macleod was engineer officer of the destroyer *Escapade*. In September 1943 she was escorting a Canada bound convoy under attack by a pack of U-boats using acoustic torpedoes. At around midnight in mid- Atlantic she attacked a firm contact with the newly installed Hedgehog mortar, which promptly exploded on its mounting, destroying the bridge and breaking the ship's back. Of the officers, only a newly promoted Lieutenant R.N.V.R., the doctor and Kenneth were not dead or seriously wounded.

After the fires had been extinguished and much shoring up, Kenneth describes how his colleague, Wilf Homer, pinned the one remaining chart to a board on top of the wardroom bath. The only land featured was Iceland. The magnetic compass on the searchlight platform had not been swung in living memory and the bows tended to roll to port when the rest of the hull rolled to starboard. Nevertheless they steamed the badly damaged ship back to fight another day. Worth remembering that the average age of all these heroes was about twenty and much less if you add in ships' companies.

Sadly there is no time for our own submarines' huge contribution: or how Lieutenant (now Rear Admiral Sir) David Scott in *Seraph* helped to land "the man who never was" in Spain with an unpaid Gieves Bill in the dressed up stiff's pocket, Royal Marine uniform and all. Or Terry Lewin's description of the first United States Navy convoy action in which his ship *Highlander* was involved. Or even U.S.N. Admiral Hal Shear's driving the machinery of U.S.S. *Stack* at forty knots (this future C.-in-C. Southern Europe was the engineer), to escort the *Queen Mary* with 20,000 troops to the invasion of North Africa. Or midshipman Darby George, now Captain, on the death of the *Bismarck*.

Western approaches H.Q. was not easily put out. But the following from an American ally: "Have sunk U-boat, where am I?" generated some surprise. Back went a dead pan "your position is lat. and long. so and so." Shortly after came "have sunk second U-boat, where am I now?" The penny dropped – "top of the class."

It is good to hear that at long last Liverpool now has a Battle of the Atlantic Museum, which should draw attention to the Fiftieth Anniversary. This was no Battle of Britain, it was the Battle for Britain.

Subsequently reprinted in The Naval Review, The Naval Historical Collectors and Research Association Review and The London Flotilla Bulletin.

Notes

Chapter 1.

1. Lt. Commander J.G.W. Deneys.
2. Royal Naval College, Dartmouth. Cadets joined via a competitive examination at thirteen.
3. Currently open to the public near Tower Bridge. 1993.
4. Article by author, 'Riddle of the Sound', *Naval Review*, October 1991.
5. Admiral of the Fleet Lord Lewin of Greenwich, K.G., G.C.B., M.V.O., D.S.C., later First Sea Lord and Chief of Defence Staff.
6. Admiral Sir Henry Rawlings, later commanded Cruiser squadron in evacuation of army from Crete and then second in command British Pacific Fleet.
7. Admiral Sir Peter Reid, later Controller of the Navy.
8. Correlli Barnett. *Engage the Enemy More Closely*.
9. During the delay in opening fire, while Somerville argued with the Admiralty, there was a distinct division of opinion on board. The senior officers, who had had pre-war social contact with the French navy, shared the Admiral's qualms. Junior officers, and certainly the ship's company, wanted to get on with it. (It was evident that the French ships were raising steam and preparing for sea – furling awnings and hoisting boats.) This attitude probably represented more accurately the opinion of the British public, who believed rightly or wrongly that France had let her ally down and was changing sides.
10. Midshipmen are required to keep a journal "to record in their own language their observations about all matters of interest or importance in the work that is carried on, on their stations, in their Fleet, or in their ship". In W.W.II these must have been about the only officially approved sea diaries. They are seen by their supervising officer and commented on

in the margin by the captain, who often finds the entries more of a revelation than intended by the author. On leaving *Valiant* in Alexandria we handed in our journals. They were returned by the Admiralty at the end of the war. Mine had been neatly sewn up in canvas.

11. *Valiant*'s gunroom, inhabited by three sublieutenants and about twenty-five midshipmen, was presided over by Sublieutenant the Hon. T. V. Stopford (an Etonian, nickname Uncle Terence) in an unusually civilised and tolerant manner – not at all like Charles Morgan's *The Gunroom.*

12. While the mixture of different entries to the Navy seemed to work, a public school like Fettes, tough yet philosophically versatile, may ironically have been better than Dartmouth as preparation for the W.W.II Navy, if only because contemporaries were not committed to the Navy. Even by now, both boys that I had shared a study with at school had been killed, one in an Armed Merchant Cruiser and the other as a fighter pilot. Two other friends had been killed in the Army.

Chapter 2

1. Six midshipmen shared a compartment in a vintage British-built railway carriage for a chilly night crossing of the desert to Suez, via a place entertainingly called Zagazig. For sleeping berths we drew lots between seats, luggage racks and the deck. All six survived the experience, and in years to come added up to an Admiral of the Fleet, an Admiral, a Vice Admiral, a Captain, a Commander and a Church of England parson. Memory does not stretch to recording who drew the privilege of occupying the floor.

2. The author gained a first class in Gunnery not because of a commanding knowledge of 15 inch gun control systems, but by demonstrating a loud voice on the parade ground.

3. Clydebank Engineering Co. Ltd.

4. Type 286P. The 'A scan' display was a horizontal green glow on which, if trained precisely in the right direction and the target was at the right height and made of sufficiently reflective material, a blip appeared like a weed in the grass. Range and bearing was read off against a scale. It was primitive.

5. Marc St. Hilaire method of position finding.

6. Lt. Commander, later Captain, Max Pemberton – an entertaining and imaginative instructor in an expertise wilfully neglected by the Royal Navy after W.W.I until the German U boat for the second time drew attention to it.

7. The nearest flotilla staff was at Sheerness, but only when the Destroyer Leader was in harbour.

8. Later Vice Admiral Sir James Troup, Flag Officer Clyde.
9. Some of these anecdotes centred on an eccentric ship master called Wallis, who kept his socks up with lamp wick. Four years later the author ran into a grizzled Boom Defence Officer in Ceylon, and addressed him by name without introduction, having identified him by his garters.
10. Later Rear Admiral Derek Kent.
11. Dockyard workmen still on board. Heavy seas penetrated the unfinished 4.5 inch casemates which were awash. We evidently missed Bermuda, which is a flat island. The captain saw his midshipmen shooting evening stars and commented, "I hope one of you buggers knows where we are. Nobody else does."

Chapter 3
1. German fast displacement-hulled torpedo boats. Rarely operated unless wind was Force 3 or less. Enemy weather forecasts were more accurate than ours. E boats often lay stopped alongside a Channel navigation buoy for radar cover – given away by hydrophone or acceleration of propellers – and in later years by Teutonic self-evident parade ground type manoeuvring signals, which could be intercepted in escorts – though not in 1941.
2. Standard distance for destroyers at the time, i.e. one and a half cables.
3. Michael Gannon. *Operation Drumbeat*. "The British, Germans, and Japanese all practised seacoast blackout. On the Eastern Sea Frontier during the first three months after Pearl Harbour the United States practised no darkening discipline whatever" Ch. 7, p. 185. "The Americans were gracious hosts. Lacking charts for coastal waters, Hardegan, U123 took heart that he could rely on shore lights to lead him from point to point." Ibid., p. 215.

Chapter 4
1. A. Trystan Edwards. *A social study of the Royal Navy by a serving sailor*. 1940.
2. Dmitri Merejowski. *The Fore Runner*. 1902. Mahan's *Influence of Sea Power*, leather-bound two volumes, bought off a barrow in Sauchiehall Street – a Dartmouth cadet's third prize for French dated 1892.
3. Directed by Lloyd Bacon, with John Barrymore, Joan Bennett and Lloyd Hughes. Leslie Halliwell.

Chapter 5
1. Jack was put off by total incompetence, lack of co-operation and ingratitude displayed by his Soviet opposite numbers at Murmansk.

2. When Cunningham left the destroyer *Scorpion* in January 1918 he had been in command of her for just over seven years. *Sailor's Odyssey*. R.N. Destroyer C.O.s called each other by the names of their ship. *Scorpion* was probably appropriate, but how about *Scourge* or *Inconstant*? The wife of one C.O. was not too pleased to be addressed by an unbriefed American officer as Mrs. Scourge.
3. Captain R.M.J. Hutton, Captain (D) 19, later Rear Admiral.
4. Later Vice Admiral Sir William Beloe.
5. The officers' heads doors in *Valiant* were removed by shipwrights before sailing, otherwise they would have been reduced to matchwood by the 15 inch calibre guns opening fire.
6. To be fair, and apart from serious fuel deficiency, the Italian 'big ship' Navy was doing what it thought best to comply with Mahan's 'Fleet in Being'. To some extent it proved a point later in Operation Vigorous, but a surfeit of tactical retreat could not have improved morale.
7. Wardroom cooks were in those days trained separately from ship's company cooks to allow for differing tastes and life style. In the 1970s cooks became interchangeable, and in the author's view, because of the large choice in menu offered, Jack now often had it best.
8. The organisation of Fleet destroyers into flotillas (today designated Squadrons) each with a ship Leader, commanded by a Captain (by rank), with an embarked staff worked in peacetime, but was too inflexible to allow for deployment and losses in a World War. This was recognised in the Western Approaches, and easier to manage with Liverpool as a base.
9. Article 1 of the Naval Discipline Act 1866 required all officers in command of His Majesty's ships . . . to "cause the public worship of Almighty God according to the liturgy of the Church of England to be performed in their respective ships". The preliminary order "Roman Catholics fall out" was obeyed without argument in the training cruiser by Hindus, Buddhists, Moslems, Methodists and Presbyterians, who galloped off ecumenically to a refuge behind the funnel.
10. The Western Approaches Tactical Unit in Liverpool, presided over by the gifted and eloquent Captain Gilbert Roberts, was to make up for this inexcusable inadequacy.
11. Commander E.A. Gibbs.
12. Vice Admiral Neville Syfret had just relieved Somerville as Flag Officer Force H.

Chapter 6

1. Later Rear Admiral Sir Matthew Slattery, subsequently Chairman BOAC.

2. Some historians have questioned this policy – their privilege. Certainly none of us doubted it at the time.
3. Sublieutenant Roy Walmesley was killed in action and buried in Malta with the other dead from *Cleopatra*. The entry in the Memorial Book at R.N.C. Dartmouth is incorrect.

Chapter 7
1. Mr. J.C. Joughin C.B.E., R.N.C., Manager Constructive Department, H.M. Dockyard Malta, had made the vital decision to dock, instead of beach, the aircraft carrier *Illustrious*, which the author had seen heavily damaged by JU87 (Stukas) on 10 January 1941, otherwise she would have been a write off. His leadership is still remembered in Malta particularly for going in the boat to *Illustrious* with the Dockyard divers to help operate the hand pump.

Chapter 9
1. Churchill. *The Second World War*. Vol. 1V, p 157.
2. *Fortune*'s radar was incapable of discriminating features in the ragged coastline.
3. Later Admiral of the Fleet Sir Algernon Willis. An outstanding administrator – despised "Public relations" believing that if a policy was right it would be seen to be so. Uninterested in "popularity." Later, as Second Sea Lord, he directed Hugh Hodgkinson to write a pamphlet for the benefit of Reserve C.O.s (see Acknowledgements).

Chapter 10
1. In 1954 the author met Captain Kurt Wehyer in Emden. Wehyer had commanded one of these raiders, (auxiliary cruisers), ORION. He sailed from Keil in March 1940 and was at sea till reaching Bordeaux in August 1941. During this period *Orion* circumnavigated the world and created a great deal of trouble for the Allies at no great cost to the enemy – a considerable feat of leadership and seamanship. *The Black Raider*. Kurt Wehyer and Hans Jurgen Ehrlich.
2. Easter Sunday 5 April 1942. No radar was working at Colombo. At 0740 without warning a force of some 90 Japanese bombers appeared with a strong force of escorting 'Zero' fighters. Though caught on the ground, many of the 21 RAF and 6 Fleet Air Arm pilots scrambled, getting airborne as bombs were falling. Some were bounced by 'Zeros' on takeoff. Further north a full squadron managed to get airborne. At the end of the day the Japanese had lost 20 aircraft with many more damaged.

Our own losses were about the same. On 9th the Japanese attacked Trincomalee. The defences were alerted by radar. 17 RAF Hurricanes, six Naval Fulmars and anti-aircraft guns accounted for 41 Japanese aircraft 'destroyed' or 'probably destroyed'. The 70 aircraft lost by Admiral Negumo were quickly replaceable, but their crews were part of a highly trained pre-war elite. "This was a significant, but little known, RAF contribution to the Pacific War." Adapted from article by A.D.D. in *Dekho*! Journal of the Burma Star Association.
3. *Red Duster at War*. John Slader.
4. Coral Sea. Jack Sweetman. Article in U.S. Naval Institute Proceedings. May 1992.
5. It may be that this ship had been rerouted and never reached Singapore.
6. The U.S.N. had intelligently reduced the interval between boiler cleaning, a time-consuming job and particularly unpleasant in a tropical climate, from the R.N. limit of 750 hours to 2,000 by the use of a chemical additive. In spite of the advantage of an immense increase in operation time, the Admiralty sternly refused to allow this in the erroneous belief that it could cause "priming" – ejection of water into steam pipes. Later, as the result of a controlled experiment in *Victorous* in defiance of Authority, the British Pacific Fleet ordered its use unilaterally. *The Man Around The Engine*. Vice Admiral Sir Louis Le Bailly. However *Fortune*'s operational requirements forced her to far exceed every laid down regulation, which says much about the quality of her Engineroom Department and Clydebank Shipbuilders who built her.

Chapter 11
1. Mrs. Hudson-Cane and Mrs. Howard. Brackenhurst Hotel.
2. 'Joss' Earl of Erroll had been having an openly flaunted affair with Diana, second and recently married wife of Sir 'Jock' Delves Broughton. Broughton was tried for Erroll's murder and acquitted. He returned to England and committed suicide at the Adelphi Hotel, Liverpool. Subject of film *White Mischief*.
3. Civil war in Somaliland.
4. Churchill. *The Second World War*. Vol. IV. Ch. XVII p 274 and 276.
5. Later Captain Brian Gallie, R.N. Also a war poet of sensitivity.
6. *Cleopatra*, *Euryalus*, *Dido*, *Hermoine*, *Arethusa*, *Coventry*, *Newcastle*, *Birmingham*, *Fortune*, *Griffin*, *Hotspur*, *Hasty*, *Inconstant*, *Javelin*, *Jervis*, *Kevlin*, *Napier*, *Nestor*, *Norman*, *Nizam*, *Pakenham*, *Paladin*, *Sikh*, *Zulu*, *Airedale*, *Aldenham*, *Beaufort*, *Croome*, *Dulverton*, *Eridge*, *Exmoor*,

Hurworth, Erica, Delphinium, Boston, Seaham, Whitehaven, Antwerp, Malines, Centurion.
7. *Taku, Proteus, Thorn, Porpoise, Thrasher, Una* (P31), *Ultimatum* (P34), *Umbra* (P35).
8. Later Admiral of the Fleet Sir Philip Vian. "The Admiral accompanies the Fleet to sea. He participates in the dangers of battle. The men of the Fleet see the Admiral's flag floating in the breeze, and they know that he and they are comrades." *British Blue Jacket 1915-1940.* A. Trystan Edwards, himself a naval rating.
9. Convoy MWII. *Bulkoil, Bhutan, City of Calcutta, Ajax, Potaro, City of Lincoln, City of Edinburgh, City of Pretoria, Rembrandt, Aagtekirk, Elizabeth Blake.*
10. Later Admiral Sir Guy Grantham.
11. Chiefy Batt's name has been entered by a shipmate in the Memorial Book kept in the Mariner's Chapel of All Hallows Church on Tower Hill near the Pool of London. This records those who died at sea and have no known grave.

Chapter 12
1. Correlli Barnett. Ch. 16, p. 509-16
2. Ibid.
3. W.W.II Casualties in the Merchant Navy were 30,248 crewmen killed or drowned in action. Correlli Barnett, Ibid. – proportionately greater than any other service.
4. Captain "Jock" Cunningham, D.S.C., R.N.
5. Correlli Barnett. Ibid.
6. Ibid.
7. An Episcopalian Minister told the author that the Theology of almost everyone at sea interested him: "God has got us into this predicament (whatever) – He may or may not get us out of it. Their prayers expect something extraordinarily miraculous – for example delivery from a lee shore in a gale."
8. Before W.W.II the author met in Edinburgh a junior Falstaff out of Egypt, who described how Farouk with his cronies would burgle the houses of rich Egyptians for fun. As a precaution the police were previously tipped off to avoid embarrassment were the Crown Prince to be arrested.
9. Operation Harpoon did better than Vigorous, getting two supply ships through to Malta at the cost of 4 sunk, 2 destroyers lost, a cruiser, 3 destroyers and a minesweeper badly damaged.

Chapter 13

1. *Living Through The Blitz.* Tom Harrisson established that it was the woman of the house who took charge when the bombs fell.
2. Officer-like Qualities' were somewhat vaguely stipulated as the aim pre-W.W.II rather than Leadership. Public school boys were for some reason assumed to have absorbed Leadership at school since it was not taught or alluded to in the training cruiser. Example counted. Only the best officers were appointed as instructors.
3. *The Winslow Boy*, a play by Terence Rattigan based on a Cadet Archer-Shee's expulsion from Dartmouth charged with theft of a postal order, which he denied. His relatives sued the Crown and won the case.
4. "Honk" – Fictitious nick name.
5. According to a medical article in *The Times*, "research suggests that this condition could be triggered by stress and emotional trauma."

Chapter 14

1. A number of her dead were washed up on the Isle of Skye, where they are now buried in War Graves.

Chapter 16

1. 7,790,697 tons over all. 1,662 ships.
2. Named after Admiral Vernon, who wore a coat made of Grogram. He introduced the addition of water to the rum ration.
3. Shackleton pre-empted a mutiny on the Antarctic iceflow after *Endeavour* was crushed by reading the Merchant Service Ship's Articles.
4. The Tot Fund was set up by the Admiralty for the benefit of Jack from the financial saving made by the Treasury arising from the abolition of the rum ration. It pays for practical amenities for ships and shore establishments, that are not otherwise provided by the Service.

Chapter 17

1. *The Oxford Companion to Ships and the Sea.* Kemp.

Chapter 20

1. A great effort was needed not to fall asleep on watch.
2. *Fortune*'s Engineer officer and Gunner(T) were both Warrant Officers. They did not have a commission and wore thin gold stripes, as opposed to the thick stripes indicating a commission. The author's commission, the document stamped with the King's signature, was dated October 1940.

3. Michael Gannon. *Operation Drumbeat.*

Chapter 21
1. A deliberate "put down" or thoughtlessness, but the C.O. would not protest.

Chapter 22
1. Ministry of Supply Regulations. *Oban Times* 19 Sept 1942
2. We never discovered what happened to her crew.
3. Not too different from how he would have been treated in U.S.A. at that time.
4. For instance A.R. Khan, later Admiral I.N. Sayed Ashan, later Admiral P.N. Vasu Kamath, later Vice Admiral I.N, and many other high quality ex-R.I.N. officers.

Chapter 23
1. The South African Women's Auxiliary Services made an outstanding contribution to looking after the entertainment of all ranks passing through South African ports. Unfortunately for political reasons no formal recognition for this hospitality was given after the war. In 1980 a *Book of Thanks* dedicated to SAWAS sponsored by the Chiefs of Staff was published by Captain E.A.S. Bailey, D.S.O., R.N. with foreword by Queen Elizabeth The Queen Mother.
2. Corvettes, workhorses of the Atlantic battle, based on a whale catcher design, were good seaboats, but supremely uncomfortable in a rough sea. *Dandelion* is a fictitious name. The incident was not.
3. Messrs Schweppes.

Chapter 24
1. *Valiant* first put out of action by an Italian Naval frogman in Alexandria, then literally fell out of the floating dock at Mombasa. Both incidents embarrassingly avoidable (hindsight), and operational effect serious.
2. This mirrored the outlook of the British Air Staff.

Chapter 25
1. The author's father came to see the ship. He was amused that the bowler hat he was wearing created activity among the workers who assumed him to be Management.
2. The author's wife, who had a job at the Admiralty, tells him that she used to wear her steel helmet in the bath in lieu of a bath cap.

3. Canadian High Commission, London.

Battle of the Atlantic: Speech by the author is included with the intention of opening a wider, yet relevant, window on the story of "The Figurehead".